DATE DUE

THE STATE-VARIABLE APPROACH TO CONTINUOUS ESTIMATION
with Applications to Analog Communication Theory

THE STATE-VARIABLE APPROACH TO CONTINUOUS ESTIMATION with Applications to Analog Communication Theory

DONALD LEE SNYDER

RESEARCH MONOGRAPH NO. 51
THE M.I.T. PRESS
CAMBRIDGE, MASSACHUSETTS, AND LONDON, ENGLAND

Printed by Publication Press, Inc., Baltimore, Maryland.

Bound in the United States of America by The Maple Press Company.

Library of Congress catalog card number: 69-11313

Foreword

This is the fifty-first volume in the M.I.T. Research Monograph Series published by the M.I.T. Press. The objective of this series is to contribute to the professional literature a number of significant pieces of research, larger in scope than journal articles but normally less ambitious than finished books. We believe that such studies deserve a wider circulation than can be accomplished by informal channels, and we hope that this form of publication will make them readily accessible to research organizations, libraries, and independent workers.

Howard W. Johnson

Preface

The purpose of this monograph is to present a theory for estimating random processes from noise corrupted observations in which they occur nonlinearly. A specific instance where such an estimation problem arises in practice is in the transmission of an analog message (voice, telemetry data, etc.) to a remote user. Typically the message nonlinearly modulates a sinusoidal carrier that arrives at the user distorted by disturbance processes encountered in the transmission medium. These disturbance processes are not always simply additive but may also, for instance, be multiplicative as in a fading channel. The user seeks to recover or estimate the original message by appropriately processing his observed data. The procedure we describe in this monograph can be applied to this estimation problem as well as many others.

We assume the observations arrive continuously in time. The procedure we develop uses the entire past history of the observations to generate a causal or realizable estimate of the desired random process, or processes, imbedded in the observations. Because of the causality restriction, the estimate can be generated in "real time" as data arrives.

The estimation procedure is developed formally by the use of state-variable modeling techniques and certain properties of continuous-time continuous-state Markov processes. While a familiarity with these concepts is useful, it is not necessary for understanding the material presented here. The reader should have some facility with random processes.

The nonlinear estimation problem to which the theory applies occurs in a wide variety of disciplines among which are radar, sonar, radio astronomy, automatic control, and radio communications. We make several applications to analog communication theory where the technique appears to be especially useful. Linear and nonlinear modulation schemes, particularly angle modulation, and continuous random channels are examined. Optimum demodulators are derived corresponding to each. We also investigate the performance of optimum phase and frequency demodulators.

In Chapter 1 we describe the estimation problem in more detail and indicate the historical relation of the procedure developed to alternative procedures. In Chapter 2 we define the estimation problem mathematically by means of an "estimation model." In Chapters 3 and 4 we associate the mathematical development of the theory with this model. In Chapter 5 we apply the estimation procedure developed in Chapter 4 to problems of analog communication theory. For this purpose, we first define a "communication model" that contains as special cases commonly used modulations and also commonly encountered communication channels. After defining the communication model, we examine several typical cases of it in detail. Finally, in Chapter 6 we examine the performance of optimum phase and frequency demodulators encountered in the examples of Chapter 5.

It is with pleasure that I acknowledge the invaluable guidance given me in this study by Professor Harry L. Van Trees of the Massachusetts Institute of Technology. His frequent discussions with me during the course of my thesis research and subsequently while preparing this monograph are sincerely appreciated. I am also grateful for the guidance given me by Professors Wilbur Davenport and William Siebert, also of the Massachusetts Institute of Technology, who served with Professor Van Trees as my thesis committee.

The work reported in the monograph was supported in part by the Joint Services Electronics Program, Contract DA28-043-AMC-02536(E), and the National Aeronautics and Space Administration, Grant NsG-334. A portion of the work was performed at the Computation Center of the Massachusetts Institute of Technology. Finally, I wish to express my thanks to the Research Laboratory of Electronics of the Massachusetts Institute of Technology for their support.

Cambridge, Massachusetts Donald Lee Snyder
June 1968

Contents

THE STATE-VARIABLE APPROACH TO CONTINUOUS ESTIMATION

1. Introduction

A problem arising in a wide variety of engineering disciplines (including, for instance, optimal control, radar, sonar, and communications) is the so-called "filtering problem." It can be described by reference to the simplified model shown in Figure 1.1. A stochastic signal x(t) undergoes a memoryless nonlinear transformation resulting in a signal $h[t:x(t)]$ that is observed in an additive

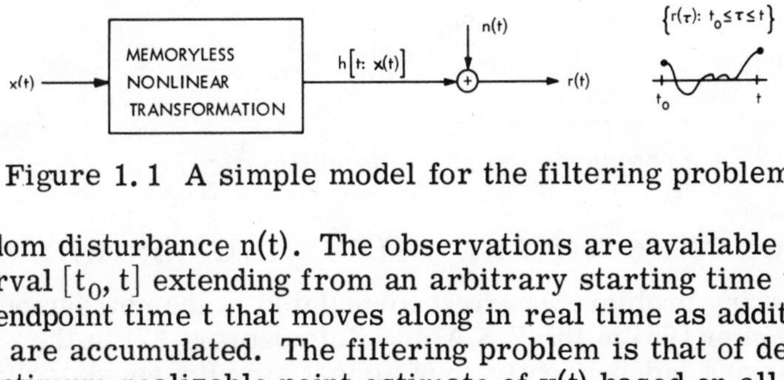

Figure 1.1 A simple model for the filtering problem.

random disturbance n(t). The observations are available over an interval $[t_0, t]$ extending from an arbitrary starting time t_0 until the endpoint time t that moves along in real time as additional data are accumulated. The filtering problem is that of determining an optimum realizable point estimate of x(t) based on all the available data, $\{r(\tau) : t_0 \leqslant \tau \leqslant t\}$.

Several terms that occur in this description of the filtering problem need to be defined:

1. *Optimum:* The estimate of x(t) is assumed to satisfy some specified criterion of optimality. The criterion we shall use exclusively in this monograph is minimum mean-square error. This is not an especially restrictive criterion because the estimate minimizing the mean-square error is often optimum for other criteria as well.

2. *Realizable:* The realizability of the estimate of x(t) refers to the fact that it depends only on the past values of the observed data. The estimate can therefore be generated in real time as the response of a physical system commonly called the optimum processor, estimator, or filter.
3. *Point Estimate:* The estimate of x(t) is sought only at the moving endpoint of the observation interval. As new data arrive, no attempt is made to return and update or improve any previous estimate.

We shall study the filtering problem using an approach based on the properties of continuous Markov processes and on state-variable concepts. The approach, which we call the *state-variable approach,* logically complements alternative approaches and, at the same time, expands the scope of the problems that can be treated. This will be evident after we first review the principal alternative approaches that are indicated in Figure 1. 2.

		STRUCTURE	
		LINEAR	NONLINEAR
PROCESS SPECIFICATION	CORRELATION FUNCTIONS	WIENER (1949) KOLMOGOROV (1941)	LEHAN AND PARKS (1953) YOULA (1954)
	STATE EQUATIONS	KALMAN AND BUCY (1960) KALMAN (1961)	STRATONOVICH (1960) KUSHNER (1964)

Figure 1. 2 Approaches to continuous estimation.

1.1 APPROACHES TO THE FILTERING PROBLEM

The filtering problem was first formulated in the now famous studies of Wiener [65] in the U.S.A. and Kolmogorov [27] in the U.S.S.R. Working independently, they almost simultaneously solved the "linear" filtering problem in which the criterion of optimality requires that the estimate of x(t) be the *linear* transformation of r(t) that minimizes the mean-square estimation error. Within the framework of the Wiener-Kolmogorov theory, all random processes are characterized by correlation functions. No other statistical properties of the processes are required or, for that matter, used if known. The optimum linear filter whose output is the desired estimate, when the input is r(t), is specified in terms of the known correlation functions by an integral equation called the Wiener-Hopf equation.

The linearity restriction imposed by Wiener and Kolmogorov is severe in some applications. However, it can be demonstrated that when x(t) and n(t) are sample functions from a Gaussian process and, in addition, h[t : x(t)] is a linear function of x(t), the minimum mean-square error estimate of x(t) is generated by a linear transformation of r(t). In this instance, there is no penalty for imposing the linearity restriction, and the desired linear transformation is obtained from the solution to the Wiener-Hopf equation. On the other hand, if either x(t) or n(t) is non-Gaussian or if h[t : x(t)] is a nonlinear transformation of x(t), then a nonlinear transformation of r(t) may provide a better estimate than the linear transformation obtained by solving the Wiener-Hopf equation.

An alternative theory not having the linearity restriction has been proposed by Lehan and Parks [35] and Youla [69]. With this theory, x(t) and n(t) are required to be sample functions from a Gaussian process—this is the price paid for removing the linearity restriction. The two processes are still described by correlation functions and the estimate resulting from the theory is specified in terms of these functions by an integral equation. In general, the estimate is generated by a nonlinear transformation of r(t) whenever h[t : x(t)] is a nonlinear function of x(t).

Lehan and Parks formulate their theory by first imbedding the filtering problem in a more general interval estimation problem in which the entire waveform $\{x(\tau) : t_0 \leq \tau \leq t\}$ is estimated based on the entire observed waveform $\{r(\tau) : t_0 \leq \tau \leq t\}$. The estimate of x(t), at time t, is extracted from the interval estimate by looking at the endpoint. Unfortunately, the integral equation for the interval estimate cannot generally be implemented because, as observed by Van Trees [58, 60], its solution corresponds to the response of a nonlinear physically unrealizable feedback system to the observed waveform.

The theories of Wiener-Kolmogorov and Lehan-Parks-Youla are similar in two respects. For each, random processes are specified in terms of correlation functions and estimates are expressed in terms of these functions by integral equations.

In 1960, Kalman and Bucy [26] presented a new approach to the linear filtering problem. The novelty of their formulation was the representation of all random processes by differential or state equations rather than correlation functions. By restricting their attention to Gaussian-Markov processes in particular, they derived differential equations for the estimate. These equations can be used to construct a linear processor that is, of course, identical to the one specified by the Wiener-Hopf equation. However, there is a definite practical advantage in having a differential equation for the *estimate* instead of an integral equation for the *processor*. Specifically, it is much easier to solve a differential equation by analog or digital techniques than to solve an integral equation and then perform a convolution.

The approach to the filtering problem we describe in the sequel has its origin in the works of Stratonovich [49] of the U.S.S.R. and Kushner [32] of the U.S.A. It logically complements the alternative approaches indicated in Figure 1.2 of Wiener-Kolmogorov, Kalman-Bucy, and Lehan-Parks-Youla. A state representation is used for all random processes and there is no linearity restriction, therefore the processor may turn out to be nonlinear. The estimate is described by a differential equation, hence the computational advantages that accrue with Kalman-Bucy filtering carry over to the nonlinear case. In addition, the state-variable approach is in a sense more general than the approaches it complements. As will be seen in Chapter 2, the random processes included in the formulation are continuous Markov processes of which Gaussian-Markov processes are a special case.

1.2 APPLICATIONS

The state-variable approach can be applied in many diverse disciplines where the filtering problem arises, so to present it first in a general context, we define an *estimation model* and associate with it the formal mathematical development of the theory. Applications are then made to analog communication theory in order to illustrate the usefulness of the approach in modulation-demodulation theory. For this purpose a broad *communication model* is defined for representing analog communication over randomly time-varying channels. It is a special case of the estimation model and can represent such linear and nonlinear modulation schemes as AM, PM, FM, pre-emphasized FM, and PM_n/PM; and such continuous channels as additive noise channels, Rayleigh and Rician channels, fixed channels with memory, and multilink channels. Consideration is given to several of these cases with special emphasis on estimating stochastic messages transmitted by PM and FM. We shall also investigate the performance of the optimum PM and FM demodulators resulting from the theory.

Additional applications of the state-variable approach are mentioned in connection with the identification of linear systems in real time. Such identification problems arise in the communication theory context when it is desired to estimate parameters of a random channel, a correlation function, or a spectral density in real time. With the state-variable approach, this can be done while simultaneously estimating analog messages.

Several applications to problems arising in control theory are available in the references mentioned in the next section.

1.3 PREVIOUS RELATED STUDIES

The state-variable approach has its origin in the works of Stratonovich [49] and Kushner [32]. We make extensive use of Kushner's work. His equation for the conditional probability density of a Markov process observed in noise is our point of departure. Following Kushner, we also use the Ito calculus [23, 38] rather than the alternative calculus recently developed by Stratonovich [50].

Discrete counterparts to the filtering problem, which we shall formulate in Chapter 2, or to special cases of it, have been studied by Wonham [66, 67], Weaver [64], Cox [10, 11], Mowery [37], and Ho and Lee [22].

Special cases of the continuous model have also been studied. Kalman [25] and Kalman and Bucy [26] considered the estimation of linearly transformed Gaussian-Markov processes. Smith, et al. [39], McLean, et al. [36], and Battin [4] used the Kalman-Bucy equations for the estimation of nonlinearly transformed Markov processes by initially linearizing all associated equations; these three papers are among the earliest of many describing this approach. Cox [10] used a technique of linearization and dynamic programming and arrived at the same estimation equations as Smith, McLean, and Battin. Bucy [9] examined the estimation of nonlinearly transformed one-dimensional Markov processes by approximating the conditional mean. Snyder [41, 43] also used approximations to the conditional mean in the initial studies leading the results presented here. Similarly, Fisher [20], Bass, et al. [3], and Jazwinski [24] considered approximations to the conditional mean—Fisher also discusses various other approximations and their effects. Detchmendy and Sridar [14] studied the filtering problem using dynamic programming and invariant imbedding and arrived at equations equivalent to those of Chapter 4. Several related, not widely known studies have been made in the U.S.S.R. [7, 8, 29, 30, 46 to 50, 54]. These are generally for the case of nonlinearly transformed one-dimensional Markov processes.

Application of state-variable estimation procedures to communication theory are given by Weaver [64], Snyder [41, 43, 45], and in the cited references from the U.S.S.R.

Van Trees [56, 58 to 60] and Thomas and Wong [51], among many others, have used Youla's approach [69] to study communication models that are special cases of our model of Chapter 5. We shall indicate briefly the relationship between their demodulators and ours. Recall that the alternative approach leads to an integral equation for the estimate and that the equation corresponds to a physically unrealizable demodulator. Van Trees [58, 60] suggests making an approximation to the unrealizable demodulator for the purpose of implementation. It consists of a cascade of a nonlinear physically realizable demodulator and a physically unrealizable linear filter. On the other hand, the state-variable approach leads directly to a physically realizable demodulator. It is equivalent to the nonlinear physically realizable portion of the cascade approximation suggested by Van Trees.

1.4 ORGANIZATION

Chapters 2, 3, and 4 are devoted to the mathematical development of the state-variable approach to the filtering problem. The estimation model that describes the problem in general terms is defined in Chapter 2. An equation for the conditional probability density of a Markov process observed in noise is derived in Chapter 3. The equation for the optimum and quasi-optimum estimate of a Markov process observed in noise are derived in Chapter 4.

The first part of Chapter 5 contains the definition of the communication model and a discussion relating this model to the estimation model of Chapter 2. The remainder of the chapter contains a variety of examples that serve to illustrate the broad scope of the approach when applied to analog communication theory.

Chapter 6 contains the results of an analysis of the PM and FM demodulators derived in the examples of Chapter 5.

2. The Estimation Model

The purpose of this chapter is to define all the quantities appearing in the estimation model shown in Figure 2.1. The model is seen to consist of two parts, one corresponding to the generation of **x** and the other to an observation of **x**. The latter part is nothing more than a vector generalization of the elementary model of

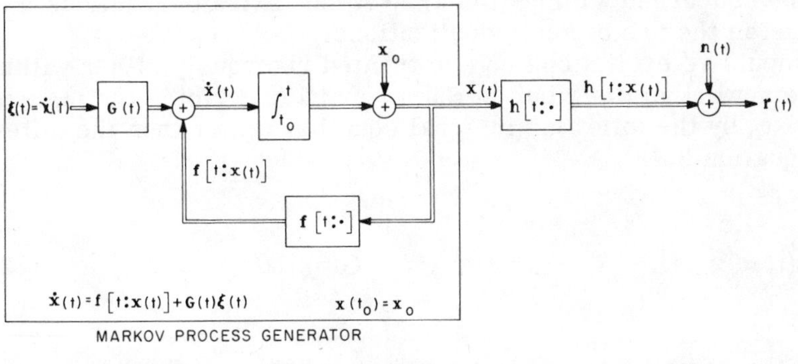

Figure 2.1 The estimation model.

Figure 1.1. The estimation model corresponds to many physical systems; however, a detailed physical interpretation is deferred to Chapter 5 where a special case of interest—the communication model—is defined and studied extensively. To give some brief indication of the role the different parts play, we mention that in communication applications analog messages and channel disturbances are represented by components of x, modulated messages are represented by **h**(t : **x**), and received signals are represented by **r**. We discuss the two parts of the estimation model separately.

2.1 GENERATION OF x(t)

The dynamic response of many practical systems is well modeled by a vector differential equation of the form:

$$\begin{aligned} \dot{\mathbf{x}}(t) &= \mathbf{f}[t:\mathbf{x}(t)] + \mathbf{G}(t)\,\dot{\chi}(t) \qquad t \geq t_0 \\ \mathbf{x}(t_0) &= \mathbf{x}_0 \end{aligned} \tag{2.1}$$

where $\mathbf{x}$ is the system state vector, $\mathbf{x}_0$ the state at $t = t_0$, and $\dot{\chi}$ the excitation. The function $\mathbf{f}$ is a possibly nonlinear function of $\mathbf{x}$ that characterizes the homogeneous or excitation-free response of the system. Both $\mathbf{f}$ and $\mathbf{G}$ are memoryless functions of time. Observations of the response $\mathbf{x}$ constitute the system outputs; these are described in detail in Section 2.2.

State space models form the basis for modern system theory. Such representations are discussed fully by Zadeh and Desoer [71] and DeRusso, Roy, and Close [13], among many others. A familiarity with the material discussed in these references is convenient but not necessary for the sequel.

As a theoretical artifice, it is frequently advantageous to employ idealized excitations, such as impulsive and white noise excitations, that are only approximately found in practice. Because we shall be concerned with nonlinear systems, extra precautions must be taken in the use of such idealizations.

Impulsive excitations can be treated rigorously either within the framework of distribution theory or by describing the state $\mathbf{x}$ for $t \geq t_0$ by the following integral equation rather than the differential Equation 2.1

$$\mathbf{x}(t) = \mathbf{x}_0 + \int_{t_0}^{t} \mathbf{f}[\tau:\mathbf{x}(\tau)]\,d\tau + \int_{t_0}^{t} \mathbf{G}(\tau)\,d\boldsymbol{\chi}(\tau) \tag{2.2}$$

where the second integral is taken in the Riemann-Stieltjes sense with χ a step function integrator.

It is also natural to employ Equation 2.2 when dealing with broadband Gaussian noise excitations by taking χ to be a Wiener process so that $\dot{\chi}$ is formally white Gaussian noise. In this case, however, the second integral can no longer be interpreted in the previous sense because almost every sample function of a Wiener process is of unbounded variation. Consequently, we use the quadratic mean interpretation initiated by Ito [23] and discussed more recently by Doob [16], Dynkin [19], Skorokhod [38], and, in the engineering literature, by Wonham [66, 67]; that is, the second integral is interpreted as the

$$\underset{N\to\infty}{\text{l.i.m.}} \sum_{n=0}^{N-1} G(t_n)[\chi(t_{n+1}) - \chi(t_n)] \tag{2.3}$$

where $t_0 < t_1 < t_2 \ldots < t_N = t$ and $\max(t_{n+1} - t_n : 0 \leqslant n \leqslant N-1)$ approaches 0 as N approaches infinity. To abbreviate the notation, we write Equation 2.2 as

$$\begin{aligned} d\mathbf{x}(t) &= f[t:\mathbf{x}(t)]\,dt + G(t)\,d\chi(t) \qquad t \geqslant t_0 \\ \mathbf{x}(t_0) &= \mathbf{x}_0 \end{aligned} \tag{2.4}$$

If $\dot{\chi}$, the excitation function of Equation 2.1, is broadband Gaussian noise, then we shall approximate it formally by white Gaussian noise and interpret the system state Equation 2.1 as Equation 2.4 with χ a Wiener process. An interpretation of Equation 2.4 in this case is that in an infinitesimal time interval dt, the state undergoes an infinitesimal displacement **dx** composed of a homogeneous displacement **f**dt and a forced random displacement $\mathbf{G}d\chi$ that is normal with mean **0** and covariance **GXG**′dt, where **X** is the parameter of the Wiener process χ. Even if the excitation is not "broadband," Equation 2.4 can often be used. For this purpose, we imagine the excitation to be generated as the response of a fictitious system. The cascade of the original and fictitious systems can then be combined as a system of expanded state dimension that is excited by broadband noise.

Of course, the notion of a Markov process is intimately connected with that of state because of the way both depend on their past history. Both are without memory given their present value. With weak restrictions on **f**, such as those mentioned below, and with χ a Wiener process, the state **x** described by Equation 2.4 is a continuous vector-valued Markov process with finite second moments. We make the following assumptions so that **x** can be a continuous m-vector Markov process:

1. **f** is an m-vector whose components are known memoryless nonlinear transformations of **x**. Further, **f** has at most a linear growth rate in **x**,

   $$|\mathbf{f}(t:\mathbf{x})| \leqslant K(1 + |\mathbf{x}|^2)^{1/2}$$

   and satisfies the uniform Lipshitz condition

   $$|\mathbf{f}(t:\mathbf{x}) - \mathbf{f}(t:\mathbf{y})| \leqslant K|\mathbf{x} - \mathbf{y}|$$

   for all $\mathbf{x}, \mathbf{y} \in R^m$, $t \geqslant t_0$, and some constant K.

2. $\mathbf{G}$ is a known $n \times m$ matrix. With restrictions on $\mathbf{G}$ similar to those on $\mathbf{f}$, here $\mathbf{x}$ is still a continuous Markov process if $\mathbf{G}$ also depends on $\mathbf{x}$. Estimation procedures can be developed for this more general case, but the generality is not required for the communication applications of Chapter 5, and we shall not pursue it.

3. χ is an n-vector Wiener process with known covariance matrix,

$$E[\chi(t)\ \chi'(u)] = \mathbf{X} \min(t, u)$$

where $\mathbf{X}$ is a symmetric non-negative definite $n \times n$ matrix. Recall that almost every sample function of a Wiener process is continuous, and it has normal increments with mean

$$E[\chi(t) - \chi(u)] = \mathbf{0}$$

and covariance

$$E[\chi(t) - \chi(u)][\chi(t) - \chi(u)]' = \mathbf{X} \mid t - u \mid$$

The independence of the increments of χ is necessary for $\mathbf{x}$ to be Markovian; the continuity of χ along with the conditions on $\mathbf{f}$ are necessary for the continuity of $\mathbf{x}$. (For details, see Doob [16] or Skorokhod [38].)

4. $\mathbf{x}_0$ is the value of $\mathbf{x}$ at the initial time $t = t_0$. We assume it is an m-vector random variable that is independent of χ and has a known *a priori* probability density $p(\mathbf{x}_0)$. However, we shall not always need such complete initial knowledge as $p(\mathbf{x}_0)$. Rather, the *a priori* mean

$$E[\mathbf{x}_0] = \hat{\mathbf{x}}_0$$

and covariance matrix

$$E[\mathbf{x}_0 - \hat{\mathbf{x}}_0][\mathbf{x}_0 - \hat{\mathbf{x}}_0]' = \mathbf{V}_0$$

are all that will often be required.

Observe that more than one vector process can be represented by Equation 2.4 by simply adjoining the individual vectors to form $\mathbf{x}$. For instance, the two processes satisfying

$$d\mathbf{x}_i(t) = \mathbf{f}_i[t : \mathbf{x}_i(t)]\, dt + \mathbf{G}_i(t)\, d\chi_i(t) \qquad \mathbf{x}_i(t_0) = \mathbf{x}_{i0}$$

for i = 1, 2, can be represented jointly in the form of Equation 2.4 with

$$\mathbf{x} = \begin{bmatrix} \mathbf{x}_1 \\ --- \\ \mathbf{x}_2 \end{bmatrix} \qquad \mathbf{f} = \begin{bmatrix} \mathbf{f}_1 \\ --- \\ \mathbf{f}_2 \end{bmatrix} \qquad \mathbf{G} = \left[\begin{array}{c|c} \mathbf{G}_1 & \mathbf{0} \\ \hline \mathbf{0} & \mathbf{G}_2 \end{array}\right]$$

$$\chi = \begin{bmatrix} \chi_1 \\ --- \\ \chi_2 \end{bmatrix} \qquad \mathbf{x}_0 = \begin{bmatrix} \mathbf{x}_{10} \\ --- \\ \mathbf{x}_{20} \end{bmatrix}$$

As a second observation, we note that components of **x** can be random variables. For example, if x_1 is a random variable, perhaps arising in a particular problem as an unknown parameter, then the first component of $d\mathbf{x}(t)$ in Equation 2.4 would be $dx_1(t) = 0$.

It is known (for example, see Bharucha-Reid [6]) that the *a priori* probability density $p(\mathbf{x}, t)$ associated with the Markov process **x** at time t satisfies the following second-order partial differential equation known as the Fokker-Planck equation:

$$\frac{\partial}{\partial t} p(\mathbf{x}; t) = L^+ p(\mathbf{x}, t) \qquad p(\mathbf{x}; t_0) = p_0(\mathbf{x}) \tag{2.5}$$

where L^+ is the forward differential operator,

$$L^+ = -\sum_{i=1}^{m} \frac{\partial}{\partial x_i} f_i(t:\mathbf{x})(\cdot) + \frac{1}{2} \sum_{i=1}^{m} \sum_{j=1}^{m} [\mathbf{G}(t)\, \mathbf{XG}'(t)]_{ij} \frac{\partial^2}{\partial x_i \partial x_j}(\cdot)$$

where $[\mathbf{GXG}']_{ij}$ is the (i, j)-element of $\mathbf{GXG}'$.

2.1.1 Generation of Gaussian x(t)

In the sequel we shall be interested in estimating scalar Gaussian processes that are stationary and have rational spectra. These processes can be represented in the form of Equation 2.4 by letting

1. $\mathbf{f}[t:\mathbf{x}(t)] = \mathbf{F}\mathbf{x}(t)$, where **F** is a time-invariant m × n matrix;
2. $\mathbf{G}(t) = \mathbf{G}$, a time-invariant m × n matrix;
3. t_0, the initial time, extend into the infinite past.

Such a representation is not unique. However, for interpreting results, it is often convenient to use a representation in which the scalar process of interest corresponds directly to one component of **x**. Moreover, when several scalar processes are represented by adjoining their individual vectors, it is convenient for each to correspond directly to one component of **x**. The following representation has these features. To be consistent we shall use it exclusively in the applications to follow. It is emphasized that the representation is not unique, and there is no restriction implied in its use.

Any stationary scalar Gaussian process x(t) with a rational spectrum that approaches zero for high frequencies can be represented by the differential equation

$$\frac{d^m}{dt^m} x(t) + \psi_1 \frac{d^{m-1}}{dt^{m-1}} x(t) + \cdot \cdot \cdot + \psi_m x(t)$$
$$= \lambda_1 \frac{d^{m-1}}{dt^{m-1}} \xi(t) + \lambda_2 \frac{d^{m-2}}{dt^{m-2}} \xi(t) + \cdot \cdot \cdot + \lambda_m \xi(t) \qquad (2.6)$$

where $\psi_1, \ldots, \psi_m$ and $\lambda_1, \ldots, \lambda_m$ are constants and $\xi(t)$ is a white Gaussian process. As is well known, x(t) can be realized as the steady-state response of the filter shown in Figure 2.2a to $\xi(t)$. Alternative realizations can be obtained by representing x(t) by any one of several possible equations of state. The particular state representation we shall use, of which a detailed account is given by Zadeh and Desoer [71], is

$$\frac{d}{dt} x_1(t) = -\psi_1 x_1(t) + x_2(t) + \lambda_1 \xi(t)$$

$$\frac{d}{dt} x_2(t) = -\psi_2 x_1(t) + x_3(t) + \lambda_2 \xi(t)$$

$$\frac{d}{dt} x_3(t) = -\psi_3 x_1(t) + x_4(t) + \lambda_3 \xi(t)$$

$$\cdot \qquad (2.7)$$

$$\cdot$$

$$\cdot$$

$$\frac{d}{dt} x_{m-1}(t) = -\psi_{m-1} x_1(t) + x_m(t) + \lambda_{m-1} \xi(t)$$

$$\frac{d}{dt} x_m(t) = -\psi_m x_1(t) + \lambda_m \xi(t)$$

where $x(t) = x_1(t)$. That this set of m first-order differential equations is equivalent to the m-th order differential Equation 2.6

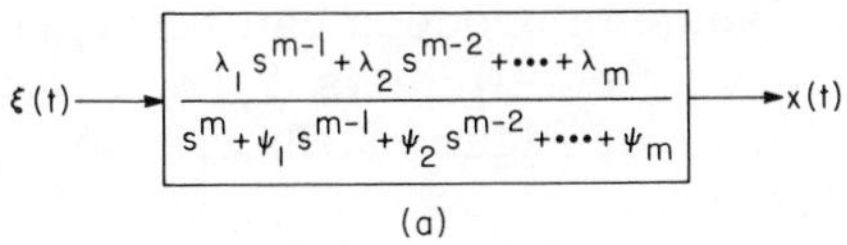

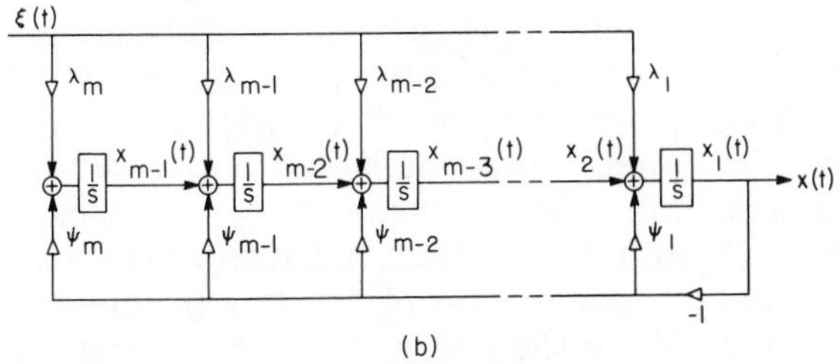

Figure 2.2 Two realizations for any Gaussian process with a rational spectrum.

for x(t) can be varified easily by successively differentiating the first-order equations.

Equation 2.7 leads to the alternative realization for x(t) that is shown in Figure 2.2b. We represent Equation 2.7 in the matrix notation of Equation 2.4 as

$$\mathbf{dx}(t) = \mathbf{Fx}(t)dt + \mathbf{G}d\chi(t) \tag{2.8}$$

where $\dot{\chi}(t) = \xi(t)$ and

$$\mathbf{F} = \begin{bmatrix} -\psi_1 & 1 & 0 & 0 & \cdot & \cdot & \cdot \\ -\psi_2 & 0 & 1 & 0 & \cdot & \cdot & \cdot \\ -\psi_3 & 0 & 0 & 1 & \cdot & \cdot & \cdot \\ \cdot & & & \cdot & & & \\ \cdot & & & & \cdot & & 1 \\ \cdot & & & & & \cdot & \\ -\psi_m & 0 & \cdot & \cdot & \cdot & & 0 \end{bmatrix} \qquad \mathbf{G} = \begin{bmatrix} \lambda_1 \\ \lambda_2 \\ \lambda_3 \\ \cdot \\ \cdot \\ \cdot \\ \lambda_m \end{bmatrix}$$

Observe that **F** contains all the denominator coefficients associated with the rational polynomial realization and, correspondingly, **G** contains all the numerator coefficients. Because of this feature, the rational polynomial representation can be obtained by inspection from the state representation, and vice versa. Also observe that the scalar process x(t) corresponds directly to one of the components of **x**(t).

A nonstationary scalar Gaussian process can be represented by Equation 2.8 with time-varying coefficients $\psi_1(t), \ldots, \psi_m(t)$ and $\lambda_1(t), \ldots, \lambda_m(t)$. The filter of Figure 2.2b with varying gains can be used to realize the process.

The definition of the Markov process $\mathbf{x}$ of the estimation model, Figure 2.1, is now complete. The procedure that has been described for generating $\mathbf{x}$ is analogous to the procedure just described for generating a Gaussian process by exciting a linear system with white Gaussian noise. Here we have formalized the interpretation of white Gaussian noise because of the extra precautions required in using this mathematical artifice when dealing with nonlinear systems and the generation of Markov processes. We turn at this point to describing the noisy observed signal $\mathbf{r}$ in which $\mathbf{x}$ is imbedded nonlinearly.

2.2 OBSERVATION OF $\mathbf{x}(t)$

We assume there are p observed signals $r_1, r_2, \ldots, r_p$ that we collect together in a vector defined by

$$\mathbf{r}(t) = \mathbf{h}[t : \mathbf{x}(t)] + \mathbf{n}(t) \qquad t \geq t_0 \tag{2.9}$$

A simple example of the type of observations of interest is provided by a phase modulation system for communicating the scalar Gaussian random process modeled in Section 2.1. In this case, we can take the observation to be one dimensional

$$r(t) = C \sin[\omega_0 t + \beta x(t)] + n(t) \qquad t \geq t_0$$

where x(t) is one component of the process defined in Equation 2.8. The reason for including vector observed signals is that eventually we want to be able to treat diversity communication systems. In these, a single message is transmitted over several channels to achieve an improved performance compared to using any single channel.

We assume a nonzero broadband Gaussian noise interference is present in each component of $\mathbf{r}$. In this case, it is reasonable to follow the previously outlined procedure and represent the observed signals by the Ito equation

$$d\mathbf{y}(t) = \mathbf{h}[t : \mathbf{x}(t)]dt + d\boldsymbol{\eta}(t) \qquad t \geq t_0 \tag{2.10}$$

where $\mathbf{h}$ is a p-vector whose components are memoryless nonlinear transformations of $\mathbf{x}$. It is assumed that $\mathbf{h}$ satisfies the same sort of regularity conditions as $\mathbf{f}$. Here, $\eta(t)$ is a p-vector

Wiener process. The process actually observed is related to $\mathbf{y}$ by the formal derivative $\mathbf{r} = \dot{\mathbf{y}}$. Similarly, the broadband observation noise is formally $\mathbf{n} = \dot{\eta}$; that is, $\mathbf{n}$ is white Gaussian noise.

Let the covariance matrix associated with η be given by

$$E[\eta(t)\, \eta'(u)] = \mathbf{N} \min(t, u) \tag{2.11}$$

where $\mathbf{N}$ is a symmetric positive definite $p \times p$ matrix. It is assumed that $\mathbf{N}^{-1}$ exists; this implies that noise-free observations cannot be made. Simply for the convenience of notation, we assume χ of Equation 2.4 and η are uncorrelated,

$$E[\chi(t)\, \eta'(u)] = \mathbf{0}$$

for all $t, u \geqslant t_0$. The extension to include the case when χ and η are correlated in straightforward.

Some statistics of the differential observation $d\mathbf{y} = \mathbf{y}(t + dt) - \mathbf{y}(t)$ will be needed in the sequel. We cite them here for convenience. The first property to be noted is that when $\mathbf{x}$, the system state at time t, is known, $d\mathbf{y}$ has a normal distribution,

$$p(d\mathbf{y} \mid \mathbf{x}, t) \sim \exp\{-\frac{1}{2dt}[d\mathbf{y} - \mathbf{h}(t:\mathbf{x})dt]'\mathbf{N}^{-1}[d\mathbf{y} - \mathbf{h}(t:\mathbf{x})dt]\} \tag{2.12}$$

Second, observe from Equations 2.10 and 2.11 that to terms of order dt,

$$E(d\mathbf{y}\, d\mathbf{y}') = \mathbf{N}\, dt + o(dt). \tag{2.13}$$

where $o(dt)/dt \to 0$ as $dt \to 0$. Furthermore, all higher order moments of the elements of $d\mathbf{y}\, d\mathbf{y}'$ are of $o(dt)$. This implies that $d\mathbf{y}\, d\mathbf{y}'/dt$ is essentially deterministic and equal to $\mathbf{N}$ as $dt \to 0$.

Equations 2.4 and 2.10 jointly define a continuous $(m + p)$-vector Markov process whose combined components are those $\mathbf{x}$ and $\mathbf{y}$. Formal division of the equations by dt results in the following equations that are represented for $t \geqslant t_0$ by the estimation model Figure 2.1,

$$\dot{\mathbf{x}}(t) = \mathbf{f}[t:\mathbf{x}(t)] + \mathbf{G}(t)\, \xi(t) \qquad \mathbf{x}(t_0) = \mathbf{x}_0 \tag{2.14}$$

and

$$\dot{\mathbf{y}}(t) \equiv \mathbf{r}(t) = \mathbf{h}[t:\mathbf{x}(t)] + \mathbf{n}(t) \tag{2.15}$$

where $\xi = \dot{\chi}$ and $\mathbf{n} = \dot{\eta}$ are formally independent white Gaussian processes with covariance matrices $\mathbf{X}\,\delta(t - u)$ and $\mathbf{N}\,\delta(t - u)$, respectively. Equation 2.14 describes the trajectory of a Markovian state vector of a nonlinear dynamic system reacting under the influence of a white Gaussian excitation. Equation 2.15 indicates that observations of the state vector are generally nonlinear and noisy.

We assume that the observed process $\mathbf{r} = \dot{\mathbf{y}}$ is available from an initial observation time t_0 until the present time t. The entire observed waveform $\{\mathbf{r}(\tau) : t_0 \leq \tau \leq t\}$, will be denoted by $\mathbf{r}_{t_0, t}$. Similarly the entire waveform $\{\mathbf{y}(\tau) : t_0 \leq \tau \leq t\}$ will be denoted by $\mathbf{y}_{t_0, t}$.

The filtering or estimation problem we wish to consider consists of estimating the Markovian state vector x at time t, based on the observed waveform $\mathbf{r}_{t_0, t}$. Note that t is the terminal point of the observation interval so it increases in real time as new data are accumulated; as new data arrive, no effort is made to return and update previous estimates. We seek an estimate, $\hat{\mathbf{x}}(t)$, that minimizes the mean-square error

$$E[x_i(t) - \hat{x}_i(t)]^2$$

for $i = 1, 2, \ldots m$, at the moving terminal time t. The expectation indicated is with respect to the *a posteriori* density $p(\mathbf{x} : t \mid \mathbf{r}_{t_0, t})$. It is known (see, for example, Davenport and Root [12]) that the desired estimate is given by the conditional mean

$$\hat{\mathbf{x}}(t) = \int_{-\infty}^{\infty} \ldots \int_{-\infty}^{\infty} \mathbf{x} p(\mathbf{x} : t \mid \mathbf{r}_{t_0, t})\, dx_1 \ldots dx_m \tag{2.16}$$

As an aside, let us observe here that the minimum-mean-square-error (MMSE) estimate of a linear transformation $\mathbf{M}(t)\mathbf{x}(t)$ of $\mathbf{x}(t)$ is simply $M(t)\hat{\mathbf{x}}(t)$; i.e., the MMSE estimate of a linear transformation of $\mathbf{x}(t)$ is the linear transformation of the MMSE estimate of $\mathbf{x}(t)$. This is obvious from Equation 2.16 and is used below, for instance, when one component of $\mathbf{x}(t)$ represents a desired analog message. An equation is derived for the *a posteriori* density $p(\mathbf{x}:t \mid \mathbf{r}_{t_0, t})$ in the next chapter. We shall subsequently use this equation, along with Equation 2.16, to derive a differential equation for $\hat{\mathbf{x}}(t)$.

3. An Equation for the A Posteriori Probability Density

With the observation of $\mathbf{r}$, the *a priori* probability density, $p(\mathbf{x}; t)$ of Equation 2.5, evolves as the *a posteriori* density $p(\mathbf{x}; t \mid \mathbf{r}_{t_0,t})$. The *a posteriori* density plays an essential role in the problem of estimating $\mathbf{x}$; we shall spend some time developing the following partial differential equation that it satisfies:

$$\frac{\partial}{\partial t} p(\mathbf{x}; t \mid \mathbf{r}_{t_0,t}) = L^{+} p(\mathbf{x}; t \mid \mathbf{r}_{t_0,t}) + p(\mathbf{x}; t \mid \mathbf{r}_{t_0,t})[\mathbf{h}(t:\mathbf{x}) - E\mathbf{h}(t:\mathbf{x})]' \mathbf{N}^{-1}[\mathbf{r}(t) - E\mathbf{h}(t:\mathbf{x})] \tag{3.1}$$

where E indicates expectation with respect to $p(\mathbf{x}, t \mid \mathbf{r}_{t_0,t})$ and L^{+} is defined in Equation 2.5. This equation was first derived by Kushner [31, 32] whose derivation we shall follow closely. The left side along with the first term of the right side of Equation 3.1 are recognized as the Fokker-Planck equation associated with the *a priori* density of $\mathbf{x}$, as given by Equation 2.5. The last term on the right represents the modification resulting from the observation of $\mathbf{r}$. When $\mathbf{h}$, and therefore $\mathbf{r}$, does not depend on $\mathbf{x}$, the last term is zero and the equation reduces to the original Fokker-Planck equation as expected.

3.1 DERIVATION

For the derivation of Equation 3.1, we observe initially that

$$p(\mathbf{x};t\mid \mathbf{r}_{t_0,t}) = p(\mathbf{x};t\mid \mathbf{y}_{t_0,t})$$

Two steps are then taken. In the first, we investigate the effect of a change in the conditioning from $\mathbf{y}_{t_0,t}$ to $\mathbf{y}_{t_0,t+dt}$ on the density of $\mathbf{x}$ at time t. That is, we examine the change in $p(\mathbf{x};t\mid \mathbf{y}_{t_0,t})$ resulting from an incremental observation $d\mathbf{y} = \mathbf{y}(t+dt) - \mathbf{y}(t)$. The result of this first step relates $p(\mathbf{x};t\mid \mathbf{y}_{t_0,t+dt})$ to $p(\mathbf{x};t\mid \mathbf{y}_{t_0,t})$ and is given in Equation 3.7. In the second step, we examine the additional change in $p(\mathbf{x};t\mid \mathbf{y}_{t_0,t})$ that occurs in $[t, t+dt]$ because of variations in the process $\mathbf{x}$ governed by Equation 2.4. The result of this step relates $p(\mathbf{x};t+dt\mid \mathbf{y}_{t_0,t+dt})$ to $p(\mathbf{x};t\mid \mathbf{y}_{t_0,t})$ and is given by Equation 3.16 from which Equation 3.1 follows.

3.1.1 Derivation: Step One

Consider the effect on $p(\mathbf{x};t\mid \mathbf{y}_{t_0,t})$ of an incremental change, $d\mathbf{y}$ in the observation vector. Clearly,

$$p(\mathbf{x};t\mid \mathbf{y}_{t_0,t+dt}) = p(\mathbf{x};t\mid \mathbf{y}_{t_0,t}, d\mathbf{y})$$

$$= \frac{p(d\mathbf{y}\mid \mathbf{x};t,\mathbf{y}_{t_0,t})\,p(\mathbf{x};t\mid \mathbf{y}_{t_0,t})}{p(d\mathbf{y}\mid \mathbf{y}_{t_0,t})}$$

$$= \frac{p(d\mathbf{y}\mid \mathbf{x};t,\mathbf{y}_{t_0,t})\,p(\mathbf{x};t\mid \mathbf{y}_{t_0,t})}{\int_{-\infty}^{\infty}\cdots\int_{-\infty}^{\infty} p(d\mathbf{y}\mid \mathbf{x};t,\mathbf{y}_{t_0,t})\,p(\mathbf{x};t\mid \mathbf{y}_{t_0,t})\,dx_1\cdots dx_m} \tag{3.2}$$

It is seen upon examining Equation 2.12 that the probability density of $d\mathbf{y}$ is determined when $\mathbf{x}$ is known and that the density is normal. Equation 3.2 then becomes

$$p(\mathbf{x};t\mid \mathbf{y}_{t_0,t+dt})$$

$$= \frac{p(\mathbf{x};t\mid \mathbf{y}_{t_0,t})\exp\left\{-\frac{1}{2\,dt}[d\mathbf{y}-\mathbf{h}(t:\mathbf{x})dt]'\mathbf{N}^{-1}[d\mathbf{y}-\mathbf{h}(t:\mathbf{x})dt]\right\}}{\int_{-\infty}^{\infty}\cdots\int_{-\infty}^{\infty} p(\mathbf{x};t\mid \mathbf{y}_{t_0,t})\exp\left\{-\frac{1}{2dt}[d\mathbf{y}-\mathbf{h}(t:\mathbf{x})dt]'\mathbf{N}^{-1}[d\mathbf{y}-\mathbf{h}(t:\mathbf{x})dt]\right\}dx_1\cdots dx_m} \tag{3.3}$$

After cancelling terms common to the numerator and denominator and defining the scalar z(dy, dt), we obtain

$$z(\mathbf{dy}, dt) \equiv \frac{p(\mathbf{x}; t \mid \mathbf{y}_{t_0,t+dt})}{p(\mathbf{x}; t \mid \mathbf{y}_{t_0,t})}$$

$$= \frac{\exp[\mathbf{dy}'\mathbf{N}^{-1}\mathbf{h}(t:\mathbf{x}) - \frac{1}{2}\mathbf{h}'(t:\mathbf{x})\mathbf{N}^{-1}\mathbf{h}(t:\mathbf{x})dt]}{\int_{-\infty}^{\infty}\cdots\int_{-\infty}^{\infty} p(\mathbf{x}; t \mid \mathbf{y}_{t_0,t})\exp[\mathbf{dy}'\mathbf{N}^{-1}\mathbf{h}(t:\mathbf{x}) - \frac{1}{2}\mathbf{h}'(t:\mathbf{x})\mathbf{N}^{-1}\mathbf{h}(t:\mathbf{x})dt]\, dx_1 \cdots dx_m} \tag{3.4}$$

An expression for $p(\mathbf{x}; t \mid \mathbf{y}_{t_0,t+dt})$ in terms of $p(\mathbf{x}; t \mid \mathbf{y}_{t_0,t})$ can be obtained from Equation 3.4 by expanding z in a multidimensional Taylor series and keeping terms up to the order of dt. Observe from Equation 2.13 that terms up to the second order in **dy** must be retained since they are of order dt in the mean. The expansion of z with terms up to the order dt is

$$z(\mathbf{dy}, dt) = z(\mathbf{0}, 0) + dt\frac{\partial}{\partial(dt)} z(\mathbf{dy}, dt)\Big|_{0,0} + \sum_{i=1}^{p} dy_i \frac{\partial}{\partial y_i} z(\mathbf{dy}, dt)\Big|_{0,0}$$

$$+ \frac{1}{2}\sum_{i=1}^{p}\sum_{j=1}^{p} dy_i dy_j \frac{\partial^2}{\partial y_i \partial y_j} z(\mathbf{dy}, dt)\Big|_{0,0} + o(dt)$$

$$= z(\mathbf{0}, 0) + dt\frac{\partial}{\partial(dt)} z(\mathbf{dy}, dt)\Big|_{0,0} + \mathbf{dy}'\mathbf{D}[z(\mathbf{dy}, dt)]_{0,0}$$

$$+ \tfrac{1}{2}\, \mathbf{dy}'\mathbf{D}\{\mathbf{D}[z(\mathbf{dy}, dt)]\}_{0,0}\mathbf{dy} + o(dt) \tag{3.5}$$

where $\mathbf{D}[z(\mathbf{dy}, dt)]$ is a column vector of first derivatives and $\mathbf{D}\{\mathbf{D}[z(\mathbf{dy}, dt)]\}$ is a matrix of second derivatives, both with respect to the components of **dy**. The individual terms required for the evaluation of Equation 3.5 can be obtained by manipulation of Equation 3.4. The results we obtain are

$$z(\mathbf{0}, 0) = 1$$

$$\frac{\partial}{\partial(dt)} z(\mathbf{dy}, dt)\Big|_{0,0} = -\frac{1}{2}\mathbf{h}'(t:\mathbf{x})\mathbf{N}^{-1}\mathbf{h}(t:\mathbf{x}) + \frac{1}{2}E\mathbf{h}'(t:\mathbf{x})\mathbf{N}^{-1}\mathbf{h}(t:\mathbf{x})$$

$$\mathbf{D}[z(\mathbf{dy}, dt)]_{0,0} = \mathbf{N}^{-1}\mathbf{h}(t:\mathbf{x}) - \mathbf{N}^{-1}E\mathbf{h}(t:\mathbf{x})$$

$$
\begin{aligned}
\mathbf{D}\{\mathbf{D}[z(\mathbf{dy}, dt)]\}_{0,0} = {} & [\mathbf{N}^{-1}\mathbf{h}(t:\mathbf{x})][\mathbf{N}^{-1}\mathbf{h}(t:\mathbf{x})]' \\
& - 2[\mathbf{N}^{-1}\mathbf{h}(t:\mathbf{x})][\mathbf{N}^{-1}E\mathbf{h}(t:\mathbf{x})]' \\
& + 2[\mathbf{N}^{-1}E\mathbf{h}(t:\mathbf{x})][\mathbf{N}^{-1}E\mathbf{h}(t:\mathbf{x})]' \\
& - E[\mathbf{N}^{-1}\mathbf{h}(t:\mathbf{x})][\mathbf{N}^{-1}\mathbf{h}(t:\mathbf{x})]'
\end{aligned}
$$

where E indicates expectation with respect to $p(\mathbf{x}; t \mid \mathbf{y}_{t_0,t})$. A typical term resulting from the substitution of $\mathbf{D}\{\mathbf{D}[z(\mathbf{dy}, dt)]\}$ into Equation 3.5 is

$$
\begin{aligned}
\frac{1}{2}\,\mathbf{dy}'\mathbf{N}^{-1}\mathbf{h}(t:\mathbf{x})[\mathbf{N}^{-1}\mathbf{h}(t:\mathbf{x})]'\mathbf{dy} &= \frac{1}{2}\,\mathbf{dy}'\mathbf{N}^{-1}\mathbf{h}(t:\mathbf{x})\mathbf{h}'(t:\mathbf{x})\mathbf{N}^{-1}\mathbf{dy} \\
&= \frac{1}{2}\,\mathbf{h}(t:\mathbf{x})\mathbf{N}^{-1}\mathbf{dy}\mathbf{dy}'\mathbf{N}^{-1}\mathbf{h}(t:\mathbf{x})
\end{aligned}
$$

where we have used the fact that $\mathbf{dy}'\mathbf{N}^{-1}\mathbf{h}$ is a scalar. Because we are retaining only terms up to the order of dt and because dt is infinitesimal, $\mathbf{dy}\,\mathbf{dy}'$ may be replaced by its expectation $\mathbf{N}dt$ as indicated by Equation 2.13. Thus, the typical term becomes $\frac{1}{2}\mathbf{h}'\mathbf{N}^{-1}\mathbf{h}\,dt$. This procedure can be repeated for other terms associated with $\mathbf{D}\{\mathbf{D}[z(\mathbf{dy}, dt)]\}_{0,0}$.

The result of substituting the individual terms into Equation 3.5 is

$$
\begin{aligned}
z(\mathbf{dy}, dt) = {} & 1 + \mathbf{dy}'\mathbf{N}^{-1}\mathbf{h}(t:\mathbf{x}) - \mathbf{dy}'\mathbf{N}^{-1}[E\mathbf{h}(t:\mathbf{x})] \\
& - \mathbf{h}'(t:\mathbf{x})\mathbf{N}^{-1}[E\mathbf{h}(t:\mathbf{x})]dt + [E\mathbf{h}(t:\mathbf{x})]'\mathbf{N}^{-1}[E\mathbf{h}(t:\mathbf{x}]dt + o(dt)
\end{aligned}
$$

Hence

$$
z(\mathbf{dy}, dt) = 1 + [\mathbf{dy} - E\mathbf{h}(t:\mathbf{x})dt]'\mathbf{N}^{-1}[\mathbf{h}(t:\mathbf{x}) - E\mathbf{h}(t:\mathbf{x})] + o(dt) \tag{3.6}
$$

where E indicates expectation with respect to $p(\mathbf{x}; t \mid \mathbf{y}_{t_0,t})$.

By using the definition of z from Equation 3.4, we conclude that the effect of an incremental observation $\mathbf{dy}$ is, to terms of order dt, an incremental change in $p(\mathbf{x}; t \mid \mathbf{y}_{t_0,t})$ given by

$$
\begin{aligned}
& p(\mathbf{x}; t \mid \mathbf{y}_{t_0,t+dt}) - p(\mathbf{x}; t \mid \mathbf{y}_{t_0,t}) \\
& \quad = p(\mathbf{x}; t \mid \mathbf{y}_{t_0,t})[\mathbf{h}(t:\mathbf{x}) - E\mathbf{h}(t:\mathbf{x})]'\mathbf{N}^{-1}[\mathbf{dy} - E\mathbf{h}(t:\mathbf{x})dt] + o(dt)
\end{aligned} \tag{3.7}
$$

3.1.2 Derivation: Step Two

For convenience, let the right side of Equation 3.7 be abbreviated by $dq(t:\mathbf{x})$. Then

$$p(\mathbf{x};t \mid \mathbf{y}_{t_0,t+dt}) = p(\mathbf{x};t \mid \mathbf{y}_{t_0,t}, \mathbf{dy}) = p(\mathbf{x};t \mid \mathbf{y}_{t_0,t}) + dq(t:\mathbf{x}) + o(dt) \tag{3.8}$$

The effect on the conditional probability density of an incremental change in $\mathbf{x}$ will now be examined. The derivation closely parallels that usually given for the Fokker-Planck equation, Equation 2.5.

Observe initially that

$$p(\mathbf{x};t+dt \mid \mathbf{y}_{t_0,t+dt})$$

$$= \int_{-\infty}^{\infty}\cdots\int_{-\infty}^{\infty} p(\mathbf{x};t+dt \mid \mathbf{u};t,\mathbf{y}_{t_0,t},\mathbf{dy})\, p(\mathbf{u};t \mid \mathbf{y}_{t_0,t+dt})\, du_1 \cdots du_m$$

$$= \int_{-\infty}^{\infty}\cdots\int_{-\infty}^{\infty} p(\mathbf{x};t+dt \mid \mathbf{u};t)\, p(\mathbf{u};t \mid \mathbf{y}_{t_0,t+dt})\, du_1 \cdots du_m \tag{3.9}$$

where $p(\mathbf{x};t+dt \mid \mathbf{u};t)$ is the transition probability associated with the Markov process $\mathbf{x}(t)$ and $\mathbf{x}$ and $\mathbf{u}$ are the realizations of the process at times $t+dt$ and t, respectively. Use has been made of the fact that when $\mathbf{x}(t)=\mathbf{u}$ is known, no information about $\mathbf{x}(t+dt)=\mathbf{x}$ is provided by either $\mathbf{y}_{t_0,t}$ or $\mathbf{dy}$. This is because, $\mathbf{y}_{t_0,t}$, which depends only on the past of $\mathbf{x}(t)$ before time t, provides no information because of the Markovian nature of $\mathbf{x}(t)$. In addition, $\mathbf{dy} = \mathbf{h}[t:\mathbf{x}(t)]\,dt + d\eta(t)$ provides no additional information because of the assumed independence of $\chi(t)$ and $\eta(t)$.

Let $a(\mathbf{x})$ be an arbitrary function possessing a multidimensional Taylor expansion,

$$a(\mathbf{x}) = a(\mathbf{u}) + \sum_{i=1}^{m}(x_i - u_i)\left.\frac{\partial a(\mathbf{x})}{\partial x_i}\right|_{\mathbf{u}}$$

$$+\frac{1}{2}\sum_{i=1}^{m}\sum_{j=1}^{m}(x_i-u_i)(x_j-u_j)\left.\frac{\partial^2 a(\mathbf{x})}{\partial x_i\,\partial x_j}\right|_{\mathbf{u}} + \cdots \tag{3.10}$$

This function enters only in intermediate steps and not in the final result. Because $x_i - u_i = dx_i = f_i(t:\mathbf{u})dt + d\chi_i$, we have

$$E[x_i - u_i] = f_i(t:\mathbf{u})dt \tag{3.11}$$

and

$$E[x_i - u_i][x_j - u_j] = [\mathbf{G}(t)\mathbf{X}\mathbf{G}'(t)]_{ij}\,dt$$

where E indicates expectation with respect to $p(\mathbf{x}; t + dt \mid \mathbf{u}; t)$. All higher order moments of $(x_i - u_i)$ are of order greater than dt. Therefore, terms in the expansion of $a(\mathbf{x})$ beyond the second derivative can be neglected.

We now multiply both sides of Equation 3.9 by $a(\mathbf{x})$ and integrate. The result is

$$\int_{-\infty}^{\infty}\cdots\int_{-\infty}^{\infty} a(\mathbf{x})\, p(\mathbf{x}; t + dt \mid \mathbf{y}_{t_0, t+dt})\, dx_1 \cdots dx_m$$
$$= \int_{-\infty}^{\infty}\cdots\int_{-\infty}^{\infty} a(\mathbf{x}) p(\mathbf{x}; t + dt \mid \mathbf{u}; t)$$
$$\times\, p(\mathbf{u}; t \mid \mathbf{y}_{t_0, t+dt})\, du_1 \cdots du_m\, dx_1 \cdots dx_m \qquad (3.12)$$

If we substitute the expansion for $a(\mathbf{x})$ into the right side of Equation 3.12 and integrate with respect to $\mathbf{x}$, using Equation 3.11, and keep terms to the order of dt, we have

$$\int_{-\infty}^{\infty}\cdots\int_{-\infty}^{\infty} a(\mathbf{x})\; p(\mathbf{x}; t + dt \mid \mathbf{y}_{t_0, t+dt})\, dx_1 \cdots dx_m$$
$$= \int_{-\infty}^{\infty}\cdots\int_{-\infty}^{\infty} \left\{ a(\mathbf{u}) + \sum_{i=1}^{m} f_i(t:\mathbf{u}) \left.\frac{\partial a(\mathbf{x})}{\partial x_i}\right|_{\mathbf{u}} dt \right.$$
$$\left. + \frac{1}{2}\sum_{i=1}^{m}\sum_{j=1}^{m} [\mathbf{G}(t)\,\mathbf{XG}'(t)]_{ij} \left.\frac{\partial^2 a(\mathbf{x})}{\partial x_i \partial x_j}\right|_{\mathbf{u}} dt \right\} p(\mathbf{u}; t \mid \mathbf{y}_{t_0, t+dt}) du_1 \cdots du_m$$
$$+ o(dt) \qquad (3.13)$$

We obtain the final result by integrating the last two terms on the right by parts. Provided $a(\mathbf{x})$ is such that all the functions $f_i pa$, $(\mathbf{GXG}')_{ij}\, p\, \partial a/\partial x_i$, $(\mathbf{GXG})_{ij}\, a\, \partial p/\partial x_j$, for $i, j = 1, 2, \ldots, m$, are zero when any one of their arguments is unbounded, the result we obtain, after changing integration variables from $\mathbf{u}$ to $\mathbf{x}$, is

$$\int_{-\infty}^{\infty}\cdots\int_{-\infty}^{\infty} a(\mathbf{x})\, p(\mathbf{x}; t + dt \mid \mathbf{y}_{t_0, t+dt})\, dx_1 \ldots dx_m$$
$$= \int_{-\infty}^{\infty}\cdots\int_{-\infty}^{\infty} a(\mathbf{x})[p(\mathbf{x}; t \mid \mathbf{y}_{t_0, t+dt})$$
$$- \sum_{i=1}^{m} \frac{\partial}{\partial x_i} [f_i(t:\mathbf{x})\, p(\mathbf{x}; t \mid \mathbf{y}_{t_0, t+dt})]dt$$
$$+ \frac{1}{2}\sum_{i=1}^{m}\sum_{j=1}^{m} [\mathbf{G}(t)\,\mathbf{XG}'(t)]_{ij} \frac{\partial^2}{\partial x_i \partial x_j}\, p(\mathbf{x}; t \mid \mathbf{y}_{t_0, t+dt}) dt]\, dx_1 \cdots dx_m$$
$$+ o(dt) \qquad (3.14)$$

Finally, we use the arbitrariness of $a(\mathbf{x})$ and the expression for $p(\mathbf{x}; t \mid \mathbf{y}_{t_0, t+dt})$ of Equation 3.8 to conclude

$$p(\mathbf{x}; t + dt \mid \mathbf{y}_{t_0, t+dt}) - p(\mathbf{x}; t \mid \mathbf{y}_{t_0, t})$$

$$= dq(t:\mathbf{x}) - \sum_{i=1}^{m} \frac{\partial}{\partial x_i}[f_i(t:\mathbf{x})\, p(\mathbf{x}; t \mid \mathbf{y}_{t_0, t})]dt$$

$$+ \frac{1}{2} \sum_{i=1}^{m} \sum_{j=1}^{m} [G(t)XG'(t)]_{ij} \frac{\partial^2}{\partial x_i \partial x_j} p(\mathbf{x}; t \mid \mathbf{y}_{t_0, t})dt + o(dt) \qquad (3.15)$$

where only terms to the order of dt have been retained. Equation 3.1 follows easily by substituting the definition of $dq(t:\mathbf{x})$ into Equation 3.15 and then formally dividing by dt and letting $dt \to 0$.

4. Derivation of the Estimation Equations

In this chapter, we shall derive the equations for the estimate of **x**. The interpretation of the equations is deferred to Chapter 5.

4.1 SUMMARY OF RESULTS

Two equations specify the approximate minimum-mean-square-error estimate $\mathbf{x}^*$. The first equation is

$$\dot{\mathbf{x}}^*(t) = \mathbf{f}[t:\mathbf{x}^*(t)] + \mathbf{V}^*(t)\,\mathbf{D}[\mathbf{h}(t:\mathbf{x}^*)]\mathbf{N}^{-1}\{\mathbf{r}(t) - \mathbf{h}[t:\mathbf{x}^*(t)]\}$$

$$x^*(t_0) = \hat{x}_0 \tag{4.1}$$

Here, $\mathbf{D}[\mathbf{h}(t:\mathbf{x}^*)]$ is an m × m Jacobian matrix whose (i-row, j-column)-element is $\partial h_j[t:\mathbf{x}^*(t)]/\partial x_i^*$. Also $\mathbf{V}^*(t)$ is a symmetric m × m approximate error-covariance matrix that is specified by the second equation,

$$\dot{\mathbf{V}}^*(t) = \mathbf{D}'[\mathbf{f}(t:\mathbf{x}^*)]\mathbf{V}^*(t) + \mathbf{V}^*(t)\mathbf{D}[\mathbf{f}(t:\mathbf{x}^*)] + \mathbf{G}(t)\mathbf{X}\mathbf{G}'(t)$$

$$+ \mathbf{V}^*(t)\mathbf{D}[\mathbf{D}[\mathbf{h}(t:\mathbf{x}^*)]\mathbf{N}^{-1}\{\mathbf{r}(t) - \mathbf{h}(t:\mathbf{x}^*)\}]\mathbf{V}^*(t)$$

$$\mathbf{V}^*(t_0) = \mathbf{V}_0 \tag{4.2}$$

where $\mathbf{D}[\cdot]$ is the Jacobian matrix associated with the vector enclosed within its square brackets.

We shall refer to Equation 4.1 as the *processor equation* and to Equation 4.2 as the *variance equation.* Observe that in general the processor and variance equations are coupled and that both depend on the observations $\mathbf{r}(t)$. The processor equation can be represented pictorially as the multiple feedback structure shown in Figure 4.1. The inner loop has a form similar to the Markov

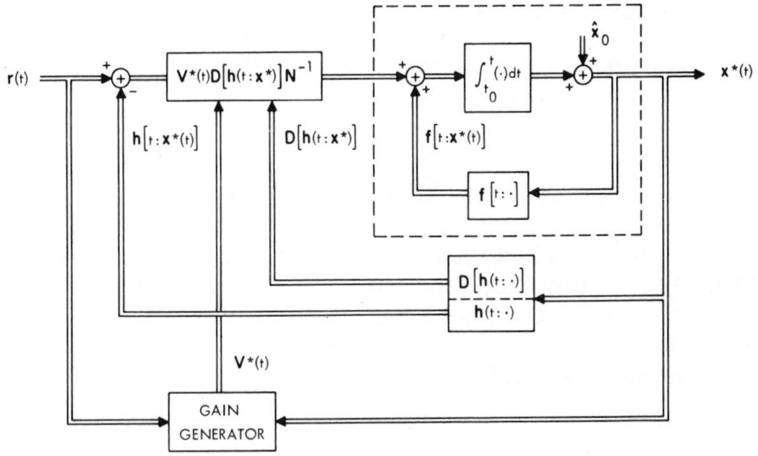

Figure 4.1 The approximate minimum-mean-square error processor.

process generator of the estimation model of Figure 2.1. An interpretation of the processor equation is that in an infinitesimal time interval dt the estimate undergoes an infinitesimal displacement $\mathbf{dx}^*$ composed of a homogeneous displacement $\mathbf{f}dt - \mathbf{V}^*\mathbf{D}[\mathbf{h}]\mathbf{N}^{-1}\mathbf{h}dt$ and a forced displacement $\mathbf{V}^*\mathbf{D}[\mathbf{h}]\mathbf{N}^{-1}\mathbf{dy}$ that depends, in part, on newly acquired data $\mathbf{dy}$. The only unknown quantity in the processor is $\mathbf{V}^*$, and this can be generated by a second nonlinear feedback system corresponding to the variance equation, Equation 4.2, and labeled "gain generator" in Figure 4.1.

Some special cases of Equations 4.1 and 4.2 are of interest. We shall mention them here.

4.1.1 Special Case One: f and h linear transformations of x

When $\mathbf{x}$ and $\mathbf{r}$ are defined by

$$\dot{\mathbf{x}}(t) = \mathbf{F}(t)\,\mathbf{x}(t) + \mathbf{G}(t)\boldsymbol{\xi}(t)$$

and

$$\mathbf{r}(t) = \mathbf{H}(t)\,\mathbf{x}(t) + \mathbf{n}(t)$$

both $\mathbf{x}$ and $\mathbf{r}$ are vector Gaussian processes. The processes are generally nonstationary, but they may be stationary when $\mathbf{F}$, $\mathbf{G}$, and $\mathbf{H}$ are constant matrices.

The exact and approximate estimates coincide in this special case, and Equations 4.1 and 4.2 become

$$\dot{\hat{\mathbf{x}}}(t) = \mathbf{F}(t)\,\hat{\mathbf{x}}(t) + \mathbf{V}(t)\,\mathbf{H}'(t)\,\mathbf{N}^{-1}[\mathbf{r}(t) - \mathbf{H}(t)\hat{\mathbf{x}}(t)] \qquad (4.3)$$

and

$$\dot{\mathbf{V}}(t) = \mathbf{F}(t)\mathbf{V}(t) + \mathbf{V}(t)\mathbf{F}'(t) + \mathbf{G}(t)\mathbf{X}\mathbf{G}'(t) - \mathbf{V}(t)\mathbf{H}'(t)\mathbf{N}^{-1}\mathbf{H}(t)\mathbf{V}(t) \qquad (4.4)$$

Equations 4.3 and 4.4 are identical to the results of Kalman and Bucy [26]. As noted by them, the variance equation for this case is a matrix Riccati equation whose properties have been studied extensively. The following properties of the Riccati equation, Equation 4.4, hold under suitable conditions:

P1. The solution can be related to the solution of a set of linear differential equations. These can be solved easily when $\mathbf{F}$, $\mathbf{G}$, and $\mathbf{H}$ are constant matrices (see Ref. 26 for details).

P2. The solution is unique and determined by the specification of an initial non-negative definite matrix $\mathbf{V}(t_0) = \mathbf{V}_0$

P3. A unique steady-state solution exists and $\mathbf{V}$ converges to this solution for any initial non-negative matrix $\mathbf{V}_0$.

The conditions under which P1, P2, and P3 hold are given by Kalman and Bucy [26]. A sufficient condition for P3 is that $\mathbf{F}$, $\mathbf{G}$, and $\mathbf{H}$ be constant matrices.

We observe that the variance equation in this instance does not depend on either the observed processes or the estimate of $\mathbf{x}$. Consequently, $\mathbf{V}$ can be determined before observations are taken. Solving Equation 4.4 for $\mathbf{V}$ involves solving $\frac{1}{2}m(m+1)$ nonlinear differential equations. A salient feature of the Kalman-Bucy approach is that the equations can be solved numerically by computer thereby completely determining the structure of the processor whose output is the estimate. When steady-state conditions exist, $\dot{\mathbf{V}} = \mathbf{0}$ and Equation 4.4 becomes $\frac{1}{2}m(m+1)$ quadratic algebraic equations whose solution is non-negative definite. The algebraic equations can be solved numerically, but for even moderate values of m a large number of decisions are required to determine the non-negative definite solution. An alternative technique is to allow the numerical solution to the differential equations to approach the unique steady-state value guaranteed by P3.

4.1.2 Special Case Two: f a linear transformation of x

When $\mathbf{x}$ and $\mathbf{r}$ are defined by

$$\dot{\mathbf{x}}(t) = \mathbf{F}(t)\,\mathbf{x}(t) + \mathbf{G}(t)\,\boldsymbol{\xi}(t)$$

and

$$\mathbf{r}(t) = \mathbf{h}[t:\mathbf{x}(t)] + \mathbf{n}(t)$$

then $\mathbf{x}$ is a vector Gaussian process. Most of the applications presented in Chapter 5 fall within this case. Equations 4.1 and 4.2 become

$$\dot{\mathbf{x}}^*(t) = \mathbf{F}(t)\mathbf{x}^*(t) + \mathbf{V}^*(t)\mathbf{D}[\mathbf{h}(t:\mathbf{x}^*)]\mathbf{N}^{-1}\{\mathbf{r}(t) - \mathbf{h}[t:\mathbf{x}^*(t)]\} \qquad (4.5)$$

and

$$\dot{\mathbf{V}}^*(t) = \mathbf{F}(t)\mathbf{V}^*(t) + \mathbf{V}^*(t)\mathbf{F}(t) + \mathbf{G}(t)\mathbf{X}\mathbf{G}'(t) + \mathbf{V}^*(t)\mathbf{D}[\mathbf{D}[\mathbf{h}(t:\mathbf{x}^*)]\mathbf{N}^{-1}\{\mathbf{r}(t) - \mathbf{h}(t:\mathbf{x}^*)\}]\mathbf{V}^*(t) \qquad (4.6)$$

4.2 DERIVATION OF THE PROCESSOR EQUATION

An equation for the exact minimum-mean-square-error estimate $\hat{\mathbf{x}}$ can be obtained in a straightforward way from the equation for $p(\mathbf{x}; t \mid \mathbf{y}_{t_0,t})$ derived in Chapter 3 by using the fact that $\hat{\mathbf{x}}$ is the conditional mean; that is

$$\hat{\mathbf{x}}(t) = \int_{-\infty}^{\infty} \cdots \int_{-\infty}^{\infty} \mathbf{x}p(\mathbf{x};\ t \mid \mathbf{y}_{t_0,\ t})\, dx_1 \ldots dx_m$$

If we multiply both sides of Equation 3.16 by $\mathbf{x}$ and integrate, we have

$$\hat{\mathbf{x}}(t + dt) - \hat{\mathbf{x}}(t) \equiv d\mathbf{x}(t) = E\mathbf{f}(t:\mathbf{x})dt + E\{[\mathbf{x} - \hat{\mathbf{x}}(t)]\mathbf{h}'(t:\mathbf{x})\}\mathbf{N}^{-1} \times [d\mathbf{y} - E\mathbf{h}(t:\mathbf{x})dt] + o(dt) \qquad (4.7)$$

Integration by parts is used and it is assumed that all the functions p, $\partial p/\partial x_i$, $x_i\, \partial p/\partial x_i$, $f_i p$, and $x_i f_i p$, for $i = 1, 2, \ldots, m$, are zero when any one of their arguments is unbounded. The expectations in Equation 4.7 are with respect to $p(\mathbf{x}; t \mid \mathbf{y}_{t_0,t})$.

We now assume that the following Taylor expansions for **f** and **h** exist:

$$\mathbf{f}(t:\mathbf{x}) = \mathbf{f}(t:\hat{\mathbf{x}}) + \sum_{i=1}^{m} (x_i - \hat{x}_i) \frac{\partial}{\partial x_i} \mathbf{f}(t:\mathbf{x})|_{\hat{\mathbf{x}}}$$

$$+ \frac{1}{2} \sum_{i=1}^{m} \sum_{j=1}^{m} (x_i - \hat{x}_i)(x_j - \hat{x}_j) \frac{\partial^2}{\partial x_i \partial x_j} \mathbf{f}(t:\mathbf{x})|_{\hat{\mathbf{x}}} + \cdots \quad (4.8)$$

$$\mathbf{h}(t:\mathbf{x}) = \mathbf{h}(t:\hat{\mathbf{x}}) + \sum_{i=1}^{m} (x_i - \hat{x}_i) \frac{\partial}{\partial x_i} \mathbf{h}(t:\mathbf{x})|_{\hat{\mathbf{x}}}$$

$$+ \frac{1}{2} \sum_{i=1}^{m} \sum_{j=1}^{m} (x_i - \hat{x}_i)(x_j - \hat{x}_j) \frac{\partial^2}{\partial x_i \partial x_j} \mathbf{h}(t:\mathbf{x})|_{\hat{\mathbf{x}}} + \cdots \quad (4.9)$$

The second term in each expansion may be written as $\mathbf{D}'[\mathbf{f}(t:\hat{\mathbf{x}})](\mathbf{x} - \hat{\mathbf{x}})$ and $\mathbf{D}'[\mathbf{h}(t:\hat{\mathbf{x}})](\mathbf{x} - \hat{\mathbf{x}})$, respectively.

The equation for the exact estimate can be obtained by substituting these expansions into Equation 4.7. The resulting expression can neither be solved nor readily implemented because of the general existence of an infinite number of terms in the expansions of Equation 4.9. It is natural, therefore, to consider the truncation of the expansions on the assumption that the components of the error vector $\mathbf{x} - \hat{\mathbf{x}}$ are small in a mean-square sense.

Let $\mathbf{x}^*$ be the approximate minimum-mean-square-error estimate of **x** which is specified by the substitution of the expansions for f and **h** into Equation 4.7 and the retention of the most significant terms. Whenever f and **h** are linear functions of **x**, no approximation is involved and the exact and approximate estimates are identical. The equation we obtain for $\mathbf{x}^*$ is

$$d\mathbf{x}^*(t) = \mathbf{f}[t:\mathbf{x}^*(t)]dt + \mathbf{V}^*(t)\mathbf{D}[\mathbf{h}(t:\mathbf{x}^*)]N^{-1}\{d\mathbf{y} - \mathbf{h}[t:\mathbf{x}^*(t)]dt\} + o(dt) \quad (4.10)$$

where $\mathbf{V}^*$ is a symmetric non-negative definite $m \times m$ error covariance matrix defined by $\mathbf{V}^*(t) = E[\mathbf{x} - \mathbf{x}^*(t)][\mathbf{x} - \mathbf{x}^*(t)]'$. The processor equation (Equation 4.1) is obtained by the formal division of Equation 4.10 by dt and by letting $dt \to 0$.

We note that the terms of Equation 4.9 having the most significant effect on the processor equation are the first two of each expansion. Consequently, the approximation is, in effect, a linearization about the current estimate. This implies that to within the approximation, $p(\mathbf{x}; t \mid \mathbf{y}_{t_0, t})$ is normal with mean $\mathbf{x}^*$.

The initial condition $\mathbf{x}^*(t_0)$ associated with Equation 4.10 is determined from the equation

$$\mathbf{x}^*(t_0) = \int_{-\infty}^{\infty} \cdots \int_{-\infty}^{\infty} \mathbf{x}p(\mathbf{x}; t_0 \mid \mathbf{y}_{t_0,t_0})\, dx_1 \ldots dx_m$$

$$= \int_{-\infty}^{\infty} \cdots \int_{-\infty}^{\infty} \mathbf{x}p(\mathbf{x}; t_0)\, dx_1 \ldots dx_m$$

$$= \hat{\mathbf{x}}_0$$

where $p(\mathbf{x}; t_0) = p(\mathbf{x}_0)$ is the *a priori* probability density of $\mathbf{x}$ at time t_0. That is, $\mathbf{x}^*(t_0)$ is the best estimate of $\mathbf{x}(t_0) = \mathbf{x}_0$ without any observations.

In the Taylor expansion of $\mathbf{f}$ leading to Equation 4.10, only the first term was retained after taking expectations on the assumption that it dominated all subsequent terms. In some applications, depending on the explicit nature of $\mathbf{f}$, it may be worthwhile to retain the second term $\mathbf{D}'[\mathbf{f}(t:\mathbf{x}^*)]\mathbf{V}^*(t)\,\mathbf{D}[\mathbf{f}(t:\mathbf{x}^*)]dt$ as well. This term is of the same order in the error as the term in Equation 4.10 resulting from the expansion of $\mathbf{h}$. Whether or not this term, or for that matter any other terms, should be retained can be answered only within the context of a particular application where $\mathbf{f}$ and $\mathbf{h}$ are specified. For the communication applications of Chapter 5, Equation 4.10 appears to be adequate.

4.3 DERIVATION OF THE VARIANCE EQUATION

We now turn to the derivation of an equation for $\mathbf{V}^*$. An equation for v^*_{kl}, the (k, l)-element of $\mathbf{V}^*$, is first obtained by the following procedure:

1. Multiply the equation for $p(\mathbf{x}; t \mid \mathbf{y}_{t_0,t})$ by $[x_k - \hat{x}_k(t)] \times [x_l - \hat{x}_l(t)]$.
2. Integrate to obtain an equation for the (k, l)-element of the exact error-covariance matrix.
3. Use the expansions for $\mathbf{f}$ and $\mathbf{h}$ and keep only the most significant terms.

Proceeding with steps 1 and 2, we use

$$[x_k - \hat{x}_k(t)][x_l - \hat{x}_l(t)] = [x_k - \hat{x}_k(t+dt)][x_l - \hat{x}_l(t+dt)] + d\hat{x}_k(t)\, d\hat{x}_l(t) - [x_k - \hat{x}_k(t+dt)]d\hat{x}_l(t) - [x_l - \hat{x}_l(t+dt)]d\hat{x}_k(t) \tag{4.11}$$

to obtain

$$dv_{kl}(t) + d\hat{x}_k(t)\, d\hat{x}_l(t)$$

$$= E\{\mathbf{f}(t:\mathbf{x})[\mathbf{x} - \hat{\mathbf{x}}(t)]' + [\mathbf{x} - \hat{\mathbf{x}}(t)]\mathbf{f}'(t:\mathbf{x})\}_{kl}\, dt + [\mathbf{G}(t)\mathbf{X}\mathbf{G}'(t)]_{kl}\, dt$$

$$+ E[x_k - \hat{x}_k(t)][x_l - \hat{x}_l(t)][\mathbf{h}(t:\mathbf{x}) - E\mathbf{h}(t:\mathbf{x})]'\mathbf{N}^{-1}$$

$$\times [d\mathbf{y} - E\mathbf{h}(t:\mathbf{x})dt] + o(dt) \qquad (4.12)$$

where integration by parts has been used to obtain the first two terms on the right. We now substitute the expansions for **f** and **h** given in Equations 4. 8 and 4. 9 into Equation 4. 12 and keep only the most significant terms. We also use the fact that to within the approximation, $p(\mathbf{x}; t \mid \mathbf{y}_{t_0,t})$ is normal with mean $\mathbf{x}^*$; consequently, odd moments of the components of the error vector $\mathbf{x} - \mathbf{x}^*$ are zero, and even moments factor into products of second moments. The equation we obtain for $v^*_{kl}(t)$ is

$$dv^*_{kl}(t) + dx^*_k(t)\, dx^*_l(t)$$

$$= \{\mathbf{D}'[\mathbf{f}(t:\mathbf{x}^*)]\mathbf{V}^*(t) + \mathbf{V}^*(t)\mathbf{D}[\mathbf{f}(t:\mathbf{x}^*)] + \mathbf{G}(t)\mathbf{X}\mathbf{G}'(t)\}_{kl}\, dt$$

$$+ \left\{\sum_{i=1}^{m}\sum_{j=1}^{m} v^*_{ki}(t)v^*_{lj}(t)\, \frac{\partial^2}{\partial x^*_i\, \partial x^*_j}\, \mathbf{h}'[t:\mathbf{x}^*(t)]\right\}\mathbf{N}^{-1}$$

$$\times \{d\mathbf{y} - \mathbf{h}[t:\mathbf{x}^*(t)]\, dt\} + o(dt) \qquad (4.13)$$

The second term on the left $dx^*_k dx^*_l = [(d\mathbf{x}^*)(d\mathbf{x}^*)']_{kl}$ remains to be examined. Using Equation 4. 10 and keeping terms to the order of dt, we have

$$(d\mathbf{x}^*)(d\mathbf{x}^*)' = \mathbf{V}^*(t)\, \mathbf{D}[\mathbf{h}(t:\mathbf{x}^*)]\mathbf{N}^{-1}\, d\mathbf{y}d\mathbf{y}'\mathbf{N}^{-1}\, \mathbf{D}'[\mathbf{h}(t:\mathbf{x}^*)]\, \mathbf{V}^*(t) + o(dt) \qquad (4.14)$$

Because we are retaining only those terms of order dt and because dt is infinitesimal, $d\mathbf{y}d\mathbf{y}'$ may be replaced by **N**dt, as indicated by Equation 2. 13. Hence, to terms of order dt,

$$(d\mathbf{x}^*)(d\mathbf{x}^*)' = \mathbf{V}^*(t)\, \mathbf{D}[\mathbf{h}(t:\mathbf{x}^*)]\mathbf{N}^{-1}\mathbf{D}'[\mathbf{h}(t:\mathbf{x}^*)]\mathbf{V}^*(t)\, dt + o(dt)$$

Substituting this result into Equation 4.13, we have

$$dv^*_{kl}(t) = \{\mathbf{D}'[\mathbf{f}(t:\mathbf{x}^*)]\mathbf{V}^*(t) + \mathbf{V}^*(t)\mathbf{D}[\mathbf{f}(t:\mathbf{x}^*)] + \mathbf{G}(t)\mathbf{X}\mathbf{G}'(t)$$

$$+ \mathbf{V}^*(t)\mathbf{D}[\mathbf{h}(t:\mathbf{x}^*)]\mathbf{N}^{-1}\mathbf{D}'[\mathbf{h}(t:\mathbf{x}^*)]\mathbf{V}^*(t)\}_{kl}\,dt$$

$$+\left\{\sum_{i=1}^{m}\sum_{j=1}^{m} v^*_{ki}(t)v^*_{lj}(t)\frac{\partial^2}{\partial x^*_i\,\partial x^*_j}\mathbf{h}'[t:\mathbf{x}^*(t)]\right\}\mathbf{N}^{-1}$$

$$\times \{d\mathbf{y} - \mathbf{h}[t:\mathbf{x}^*(t)]dt\} + o(dt) \quad (4.15a)$$

$$= \{\mathbf{D}'[\mathbf{f}(t:\mathbf{x}^*)]\mathbf{V}^*(t) + \mathbf{V}^*(t)\mathbf{D}[\mathbf{f}(t:\mathbf{x}^*)] + \mathbf{G}(t)\mathbf{X}\mathbf{G}'(t)$$

$$+ \mathbf{V}^*(t)\mathbf{D}\{\mathbf{D}[\mathbf{h}(t:\mathbf{x}^*)]\mathbf{N}^{-1}[\mathbf{r}(t) - \mathbf{h}(t:\mathbf{x}^*)]\}\mathbf{V}^*(t)\}_{kl}dt + o(dt) \quad (4.15b)$$

That Equations 4.15a and 4.15b are equal may be demonstrated by expanding the matrix expressions. The variance Equation 4.2 follows by the formal division of Equation 4.15b by dt and letting $dt \to 0$.

The initial condition associated with Equation 4.15b is determined from the equation:

$$\mathbf{V}^*(t_0) = \int_{-\infty}^{\infty}\cdots\int_{-\infty}^{\infty}[\mathbf{x} - \mathbf{x}^*(t_0)][\mathbf{x} - \mathbf{x}^*(t_0)]'p(\mathbf{x}:t_0)dx_1\cdots dx_m$$

$$= \mathbf{V}_0$$

The initial covariance is just the *a priori* covariance of $\mathbf{x}$ at time t_0.

4.4 SUMMARY AND COMMENTS

Equations 4.1 and 4.2 describe the estimate of the state vector $\mathbf{x}$ of a nonlinear dynamic system excited by white Gaussian noise. The estimate in general is only an approximation to the exact minimum-mean-square-error estimate of Equation 4.7. Alternative approximations and estimates have also been derived. In particular, we mention the work of Fisher [20] who studied a quasi-moment expansion of $\hat{\mathbf{x}}$ of Equation 4.7; this expansion has somewhat better properties when truncated than the moment expansion we have considered. An alternative approximation procedure avoiding series expansions altogether has been suggested by

Kushner [34]. Kushner [33] has also derived a differential equation for the conditional mode of **x**.

In the next chapter, we apply Equations 4.1 and 4.2 to problems of analog communication theory. The alternative approximation procedures and estimates mentioned earlier have not yet been applied to these problems.

5. Applications to Communication Theory

Several applications of the state-variable approach to continuous estimation will be given in the following sections. These applications provide an interpretation of the estimation model of Chapter 2 as well as the processor and variance equations of Chapter 4. Moreover, the broad scope of the problems that can be treated in a uniform manner is illustrated.

We shall begin by defining a general communication model that is directly related to the estimation model. Special cases will then be investigated in detail. These may be divided into three categories: (1) $\mathbf{x}$ and $\mathbf{r}$ are Gaussian processes; (2) $\mathbf{x}$ is a Gaussian process and $\mathbf{r}$ is not; (3) neither $\mathbf{x}$ nor $\mathbf{r}$ are Gaussian processes. In the communication theory context, (1) includes Gaussian message—linear modulation schemes, (2) includes Gaussian message—Gaussian channel disturbance—nonlinear modulation schemes, and (3) includes Markovian message—Markovian channel disturbance—nonlinear modulation schemes. Categories (1) and (2) can also be treated by Lehan and Parks' [35] approach to continuous estimation.†

---

† See Section 1.3 for a discussion of the relationship between this approach and the state-variable approach.

5.1 THE COMMUNICATION MODEL

The communication model is shown in Figure 5.1. Let us remark initially that the observed, or received, signal vector

$$\mathbf{r}(t) = \mathbf{h}[t:\mathbf{x}(t)] + \mathbf{n}(t)$$

is defined in exactly the same way as the observed vector in the estimation model of Chapter 2. The remainder of the communication model to the left only specifies how the vector $\mathbf{x}$ is generated. We shall now proceed through the model, beginning with the analog message source at the left, and indicate exactly how $\mathbf{x}$ is generated.

Let $\mathbf{a}$ for $t \geqslant t_0$ be the state vector associated with the analog message source of Figure 5.1.† The detailed structure of the source is indicated in Figure 5.2 where $\mathbf{a}$ is a continuous Markov process defined by the Ito equation:

$$d\mathbf{a}(t) = \mathbf{f}_a[t:\mathbf{a}(t)]dt + \mathbf{G}_a(t)d\boldsymbol{\alpha}(t) \qquad \mathbf{a}(t_0) = \mathbf{a}_0 \tag{5.1}$$

where $\boldsymbol{\alpha}$ is a Wiener process. Let the covariance matrix associated with $\boldsymbol{\alpha}$ be given by

$$E[\boldsymbol{\alpha}(t)\,\boldsymbol{\alpha}'(u)] = \mathbf{A}\min(t, u)$$

where $\mathbf{A}$ is a symmetric non-negative definite matrix. Formally dividing Equation 5.1 by dt, we have the alternative representation

$$\dot{\mathbf{a}}(t) = \mathbf{f}_a[t:\mathbf{a}(t)] + \mathbf{G}_a(t)\,\boldsymbol{\xi}_a(t) \qquad \mathbf{a}(t_0) = \mathbf{a}_0 \tag{5.2}$$

where $\boldsymbol{\xi}_a(t) = \dot{\boldsymbol{\alpha}}$ is white Gaussian noise with the covariance matrix $\mathbf{A}\delta(t-u)$.

We automatically include the possibility of more than one Markovian message, since multiple messages are accommodated by simply expanding the dimension of the state vector $\mathbf{a}$. Of course, stationary Gaussian messages with rational spectra are included as a special case when $\mathbf{f}_a[t:\mathbf{a}(t)] = \mathbf{F}_a\mathbf{a}(t)$, $\mathbf{G}_a(t) = \mathbf{G}_a$, and $t_0 = -\infty$.

The output of the analog message source enters a modulator consisting of a linear filtering operation followed by a memoryless

---

† From this point on, we will not indicate the dimension of vectors and matrices except where required for clarity. Generally, the dimensions are arbitrary with the exception of the constraints imposed by the usual rules of vector-matrix manipulations.

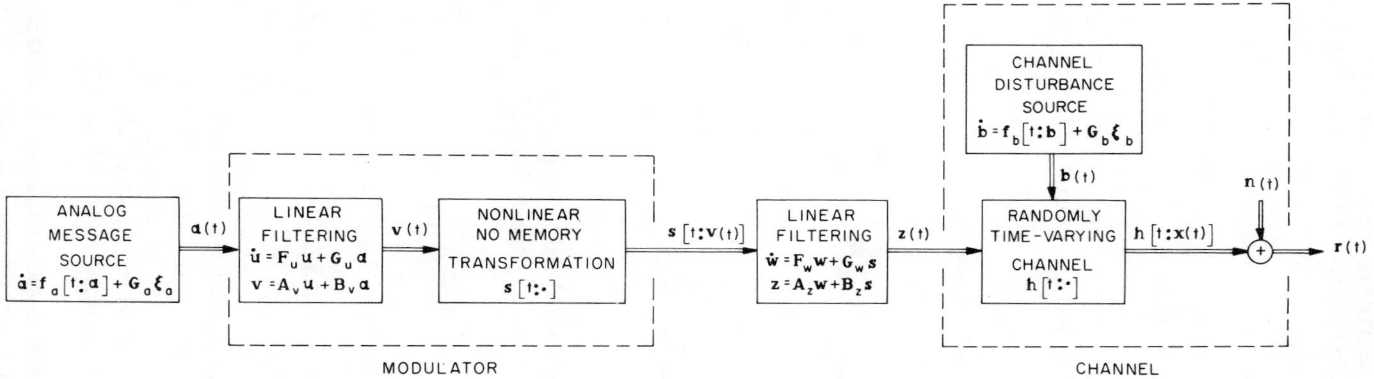

Figure 5.1 The communication model.

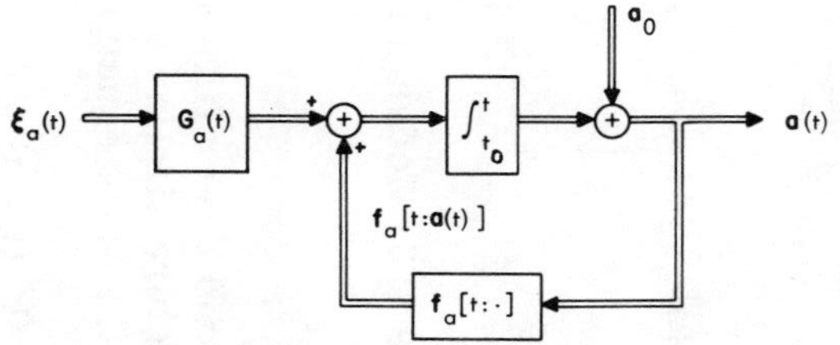

Figure 5.2 Analog message source.

nonlinear transformation. The linear filter, whose detailed structure is indicated in Figure 5. 3, is described by the state equations

$$\dot{\mathbf{u}}(t) = \mathbf{F}_U(t)\mathbf{u}(t) + \mathbf{G}_U(t)\mathbf{a}(t) \qquad \mathbf{u}(t_0) = \mathbf{u}_0$$

and

$$\mathbf{v}(t) = \mathbf{A}_V(t)\mathbf{u}(t) + \mathbf{B}_V(t)\mathbf{a}(t) \tag{5.3}$$

The output of the linear filter $\mathbf{v}$ undergoes a memoryless nonlinear transformation into a signal $\mathbf{s}[t:\mathbf{v}(t)]$ that is appropriate for transmission over the channel.

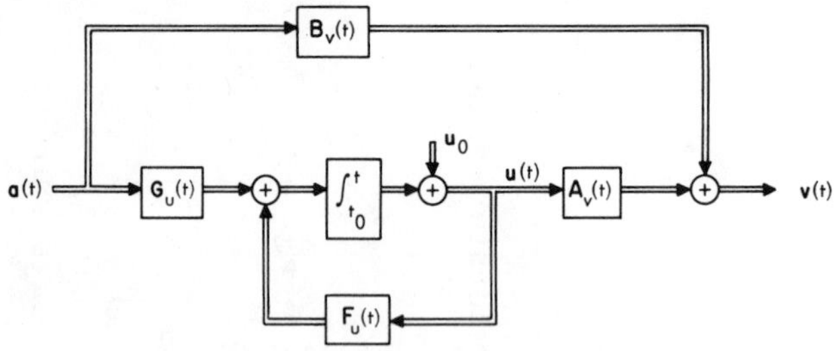

Figure 5. 3 Modulator linear filter.

A second linear filtering operation follows the modulator. It has a structure similar to that shown in Figure 5. 3 and is described by the state equations

$$\dot{\mathbf{w}}(t) = \mathbf{F}_W(t)\mathbf{w}(t) + \mathbf{G}_W(t)\mathbf{s}[t:\mathbf{v}(t)] \qquad \mathbf{w}(t_0) = \mathbf{w}_0$$

and

$$\mathbf{z}(t) = \mathbf{A}_Z(t)\mathbf{w}(t) + \mathbf{B}_Z(t)\mathbf{s}[t:\mathbf{v}(t)] \tag{5.4}$$

We shall allow this filtering to be associated with either the modulator or channel depending on the particular application. An example in which it would be associated with the modulator is with single-sideband modulation where the filter is used to suppress the undesired sideband. An example in which it would be associated with the channel is a telephone line or other link with memory.

The modulator, including possible linear filtering at its output, includes such linear modulation schemes as AM, AM-DSB/SC, and AM-SSB; such nonlinear modulation schemes as PM, FM, and preemphasized FM; such diversity modulation schemes as frequency-diversity PM and frequency-diversity FM; and such multilevel modulation schemes as PM_n/PM.

Two types of channel disturbance processes interact in the channel with **z**, the channel input. The first type **b** is generated in the channel disturbance source. It interacts with **z** in the randomly time-varying portion of the channel. The interaction can be additive and multiplicative, but more general possibilities are included, since the interaction can be nonlinear. We shall let **b**, for $t \geqslant t_0$, be a continuous Markov process described by the Ito equation

$$d\mathbf{b}(t) = \mathbf{f}_b[t:\mathbf{b}(t)]dt + \mathbf{G}_b(t)\, d\boldsymbol{\beta}(t) \qquad \mathbf{b}(t_0) = \mathbf{b}_0 \tag{5.5}$$

where $\boldsymbol{\beta}$ is a Wiener process with the covariance matrix

$$E(\boldsymbol{\beta}(t)\boldsymbol{\beta}'(u)] = \mathbf{B} \min (t, u)$$

where **B** is a symmetric non-negative definite matrix. Formally dividing Equations 5.5 by dt, we have the alternative representation

$$\dot{\mathbf{b}}(t) = \mathbf{f}_b[t:\mathbf{b}(t)] + \mathbf{G}_b(t)\boldsymbol{\xi}_b(t) \qquad \mathbf{b}(t_0) = \mathbf{b}_0 \tag{5.6}$$

where $\boldsymbol{\xi}_b(t) = \dot{\boldsymbol{\beta}}$ is white Gaussian noise with the covariance matrix $\mathbf{B}\delta(t-u)$. The detailed structure of the channel disturbance source is similar to that of the analog message source shown in Figure 5.2. Of course, as a special case, the disturbance processes can be stationary Gaussian processes with rational spectra.

The output of the randomly time-varying portion of the channel $\mathbf{h}[t:\mathbf{x}(t)]$, where **x** is defined below, interacts additively with the second channel disturbance **n**, which is white Gaussian noise. More precisely, the observed signal is described by the Ito equation

$$d\mathbf{y}(t) = \mathbf{h}[t:\mathbf{x}(t)]dt + d\boldsymbol{\eta}(t) \tag{5.7}$$

where $\boldsymbol{\eta}$ is a Wiener process with the covariance matrix

$$E[\boldsymbol{\eta}(t)\boldsymbol{\eta}'(u)] = \mathbf{N} \min (t, u)$$

where **N** is symmetric and positive definite.

In order to complete our description of the communication model, we still need to define **x**. Observe that the output of the randomly time-varying portion of the channel is a function of the 4 state vectors **a**, **u**, **w**, and **b**. Consequently, we define **x** to be the vector obtained by adjoining all the individual state vectors in any order. For instance, let

$$\mathbf{x}(t) = \begin{bmatrix} \mathbf{a}(t) \\ \hdashline \mathbf{u}(t) \\ \hdashline \mathbf{w}(t) \\ \hdashline \mathbf{b}(t) \end{bmatrix}$$

Then we have

$$d\mathbf{x}(t) = \mathbf{f}[t:\mathbf{x}(t)]dt + \mathbf{G}(t)\ d\boldsymbol{\chi}(t) \qquad \mathbf{x}(t_0) = \mathbf{x}_0$$

where†

$$\mathbf{f}[t:\mathbf{x}(t)] = \begin{bmatrix} \mathbf{f}_a[t:\mathbf{a}(t)] \\ \hdashline \mathbf{F}_u(t)\mathbf{u}(t) + \mathbf{G}_u(t)\mathbf{a}(t) \\ \hdashline \mathbf{F}_w(t)\mathbf{w}(t) + \mathbf{G}_w(t)\mathbf{s}[t:\mathbf{v}(t)] \\ \hdashline \mathbf{f}_b[t:\mathbf{b}(t)] \end{bmatrix}$$

$$\mathbf{G}(t) = \begin{bmatrix} \mathbf{G}_a(t) & \mathbf{0} & \mathbf{0} & \mathbf{0} \\ \mathbf{0} & \mathbf{0} & \mathbf{0} & \mathbf{0} \\ \mathbf{0} & \mathbf{0} & \mathbf{0} & \mathbf{0} \\ \mathbf{0} & \mathbf{0} & \mathbf{0} & \mathbf{G}_b(t) \end{bmatrix}$$

$$\boldsymbol{\chi}(t) = \begin{bmatrix} \boldsymbol{\alpha}(t) \\ \hdashline \mathbf{0} \\ \hdashline \mathbf{0} \\ \hdashline \boldsymbol{\beta}(t) \end{bmatrix}$$

† Recall that $\mathbf{v}(t)$ is just a linear combination of $\mathbf{a}(t)$ and $\mathbf{u}(t)$.

and

$$\mathbf{x}(t_0) = \begin{bmatrix} \mathbf{a}(t_0) \\ \hdashline \mathbf{u}(t_0) \\ \hdashline \mathbf{w}(t_0) \\ \hdashline \mathbf{b}(t_0) \end{bmatrix}$$

The channel, including possible linear filtering at its input, contains as special cases: simple additive channels; Gaussian multiplicative channels, such as Rayleigh channels, Rician channels, etc.; fixed channels with memory; multilink channels; and other commonly occurring channels. The Markovian disturbance processes that we include in the model have not been treated with any alternative approach.

Given all the accumulated observations $\mathbf{r}_{t_0, t}$, our objective is to estimate those components in **a** corresponding to desired messages. In addition, we may also wish to estimate some of components of **b**; namely, the channel disturbance. Note that with the state-variable approach, these objectives are accomplished by simultaneously estimating *all* the state variables in the communication model. That is, we first estimate the message and channel-disturbance processes, as well as the state of all linear filters, and then extract the desired estimates. The validity of this procedure is based on the fact that if the desired signals are given by

$$\mathbf{d}(t) = \mathbf{M}\mathbf{x}(t)$$

then the estimate of **d** is given by

$$\hat{\mathbf{d}}(t) = \mathbf{M}\hat{\mathbf{x}}(t)$$

This can be demonstrated easily with the equation for the conditional mean, Equation 2.16.

With the definition of the communication model now complete, we turn our attention to the consideration of applications. The applications presented are very simple cases of the general model that has been defined. Our purpose in examining these cases is only to illustrate the approach. In all applications using Gaussian processes, we shall employ the state representation discussed in Chapter 2, Section 2.1.1.

5.2 APPLICATIONS WHEN x AND r ARE GAUSSIAN: LINEAR MODULATION

For the following Examples 5.2.1 through 5.2.3, $\mathbf{x}$ and $\mathbf{r}$ are described by

$$\dot{\mathbf{x}}(t) = \mathbf{F}(t)\,\mathbf{x}(t) + \mathbf{G}(t)\boldsymbol{\xi}(t) \tag{5.8}$$

and

$$\dot{\mathbf{y}}(t) = \mathbf{r}(t) = \mathbf{H}(t)\,\mathbf{x}(t) + \mathbf{n}(t) \tag{5.9}$$

As will be seen, the linear observations of $\mathbf{x}$ described by Equation 5.9 model linear modulation schemes. The linear filters we get for the estimation of $\mathbf{x}$ were first derived in a general way by Kalman and Bucy [22]. We shall investigate linear modulation schemes in some detail, because the results obtained are similar in certain respects to those of nonlinear modulation schemes.

The processor and variance equations are given by Equations 4.3 and 4.4.

Example 5.2.1 Single Message, No Modulation, Additive White Noise Channel

Consider the communication model shown in Figure 5.4, where a(t) is a nonstationary Gaussian message (see Section 2.1.1 of Chapter 2) and n(t) is white Gaussian noise with the correlation function $N_0\delta(t-u)$. Here a(t) and n(t) are uncorrelated. The equations describing the model are

$$\dot{\mathbf{x}}(t) = \mathbf{F}(t)\,\mathbf{x}(t) + \mathbf{G}(t)\xi(t) \tag{5.10}$$

and

$$\dot{\mathbf{y}}(t) = r(t) = x_1(t) + n(t) \tag{5.11}$$

where $\mathbf{x}$ is an m-vector with $x_1 = a$. Here $\mathbf{F}$ and $\mathbf{G}$ are given by

$$\mathbf{F}(t) = \begin{bmatrix} -\psi_1(t) & 1 & 0 & \cdots & \\ -\psi_2(t) & 0 & 1 & \cdots & \\ -\psi_3(t) & 0 & 0 & \cdots & \\ \vdots & & & \ddots & 1 \\ -\psi_m(t) & 0 & 0 & \cdots & 0 \end{bmatrix} \qquad \mathbf{G}(t) = \begin{bmatrix} \lambda_1 \\ \lambda_2 \\ \lambda_3 \\ \vdots \\ \lambda_m \end{bmatrix}$$

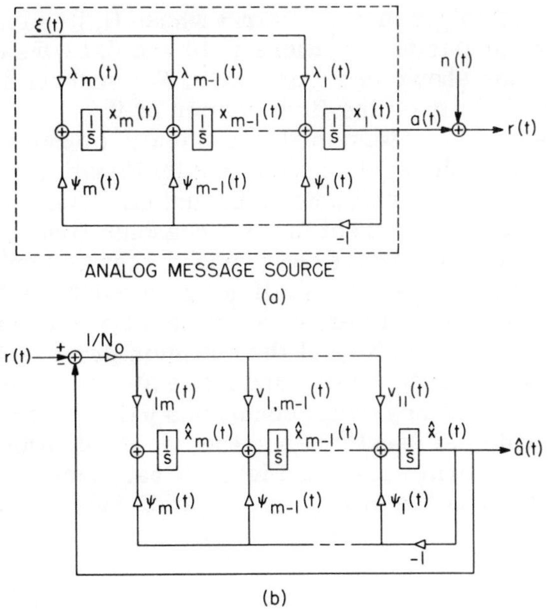

Figure 5.4(a) Nonstationary Gaussian message observed in additive white noise. (b) Optimum linear filter for estimating a nonstationary Gaussian message observed in additive white noise.

We assume that $E[\xi(t)\,\xi(u)] = X\delta(t-u)$ is known. From Equation 5.11 we observe that $\mathbf{H}(t) = [1 \quad 0 \quad 0 \cdots 0]$.

The processor and variance equations, Equations 4.3 and 4.4 become

$$\dot{\hat{\mathbf{x}}}(t) = \mathbf{F}(t)\,\hat{\mathbf{x}}(t) + \frac{1}{N_0}\begin{bmatrix} v_{11}(t) \\ v_{12}(t) \\ \cdot \\ \cdot \\ \cdot \\ v_{1m}(t) \end{bmatrix}[r(t) - \hat{x}_1(t)] \tag{5.12}$$

and

$$\dot{\mathbf{V}}(t) = \mathbf{F}(t)\,\mathbf{V}(t) + \mathbf{V}(t)\,\mathbf{F}'(t) + \mathbf{X}\mathbf{G}(t)\,\mathbf{G}'(t) - \frac{1}{N_0}\,\mathbf{M}(t) \tag{5.13}$$

where **M** is a symmetric m × m matrix whose (i, j)-element is $v_{1i}(t)\, v_{1j}(t)$. By comparing Equations 5.10 and 5.12, we obtain the optimum processor shown in Figure 5.4b. We observe that the processor depends only on the first column of **V**.

Note that **V** can be determined numerically or can be generated as the output of the system specified by Equation 5.13. If desired, **V** can be determined before any actual observations. The components of **V** are of interest for two reasons: first, they complete the structure of the processor; second, they describe the performance of the processor. We shall not give solutions to the variance equation here. Rather, we shall be interested only in obtaining the general structure of the optimum processor.

A special case arises when a and n are stationary processes and $t_0 = -\infty$ so that steady-state conditions exist. In this instance, a has a rational spectrum and the communication model has the alternative form shown in Figure 5.5a. Correspondingly, the optimum filter has the alternative form of Figure 5.5b. Let

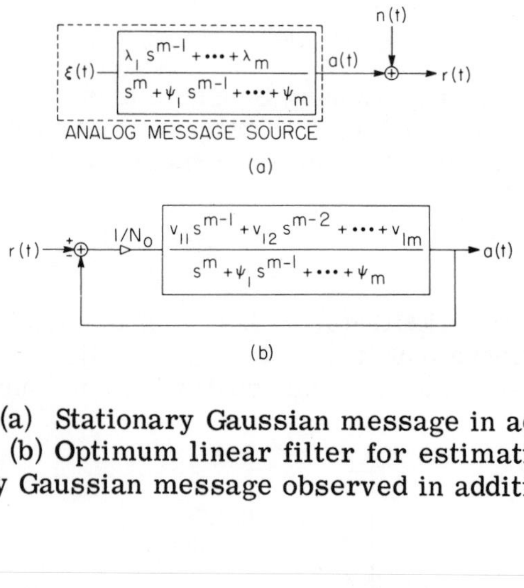

Figure 5.5(a) Stationary Gaussian message in additive white noise. (b) Optimum linear filter for estimating a stationary Gaussian message observed in additive white noise.

$G_{opt}(s)$ denote the filter appearing in the forward path. Several interesting properties of $G_{opt}(s)$ are evident by inspection:

1. The poles of $G_{opt}(s)$ coincide with those of the message-shaping filter.
2. The order of the numerator of $G_{opt}(s)$ is exactly one less than the denominator, because v_{11}, the mean-square estimation error, is nonzero.

3. The zeros of $G_{opt}(s)$ depend only on the first row, or column, of the error-covariance matrix **V**.
4. The coefficients of the numerator polynomial are error covariances associated with state variables.
5. Also, $v_{11} = N_0 \lim_{s \to \infty} s\, G_{opt}(s) = N_0 g_{opt}(0^+)$, where $g_{opt}(t)$ is the impulse response corresponding to $G_{opt}(s)$.

Properties 1, 2, and 5 can be obtained directly from the solution to the Wiener-Hopf equation [42]. Property 5 gives an expression for the mean-square error in terms of the optimum loop filter. An alternative expression, not requiring a determination of $G_{opt}(s)$ or a solution to the variance equation, is

$$v_{11} = N_0 \int_{-\infty}^{\infty} \log \left[1 + \frac{S_a(\omega)}{N_0}\right] \frac{d\omega}{2\pi} \tag{5.14}$$

where $S_a(\omega)$ watts/cps is the power density spectrum of a. We shall see later that this expression is useful in the evaluation of quasi-optimum phase demodulators. The expression was originally derived by Yovits and Jackson [70]. Other derivations have been given by Viterbi [62], Fein, et al. [19], and Snyder [40].

The structure of the optimum filter that would arise most naturally through application of the Wiener approach is, of course, the closed-loop version of the filter of Figure 5.5b.

5.2.1.1 *Special case of a one-dimensional message: no modulation.* As a simple example, consider the one-dimensional communication model of Figure 5.6a. For this case, the spectrum of a is $(2Pk)/(\omega^2 + k^2)$ and $\mathbf{F} = -k$, $\mathbf{XGG}' = 2Pk$. The processor and variance equations are

$$\dot{\hat{x}}_1(t) = -k\hat{x}_1(t) + \frac{1}{N_0} v_{11} [r(t) - \hat{x}_1(t)] \tag{5.15}$$

and

$$0 = -2kv_{11} + 2Pk - \frac{1}{N_0} v_{11}^2 \tag{5.16}$$

The solution to the variance equation is

$$v_{11} = \frac{2P}{1 + \sqrt{1 + \Lambda}} \tag{5.17}$$

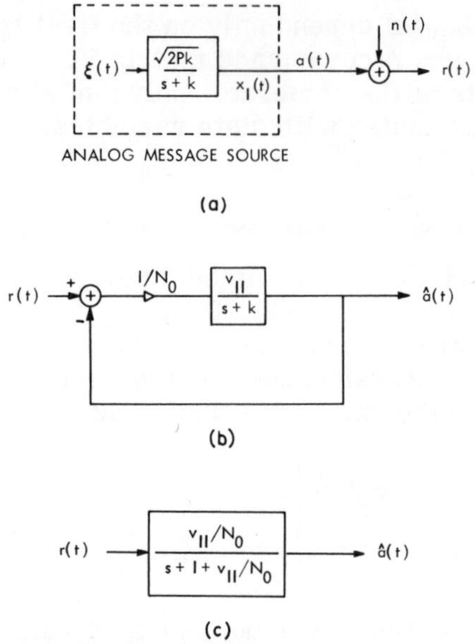

Figure 5.6(a) One-dimensional Gaussian message observed in additive white noise. (b, c) Two realizations for the optimum linear filter for estimating a one-dimensional message observed in additive white noise.

where $\Lambda = 2P/kN_0$ is the signal-to-noise ratio in the message bandwidth.† The optimum filter is shown in Figure 5.6b. A closed-loop version of the filter is shown in Figure 5.6c; this latter realization would arise most naturally with the Wiener approach.

Example 5.2.2 Single Message, Integral Modulation, Additive White Noise Channel

Consider the communication model shown in Figure 5.7a. Here a(t) is a stationary Gaussian message that is integrated in a modulator before transmission through the channel and n(t) is a white Gaussian process of spectral height N_0 watts/cps. Also, a(t) and n(t) are uncorrelated. The integration occurring in the

---

† The message bandwidth is defined to be the width of a rectangular spectrum of height $S_a(0)$ and same total area as $S_a(\omega)$.

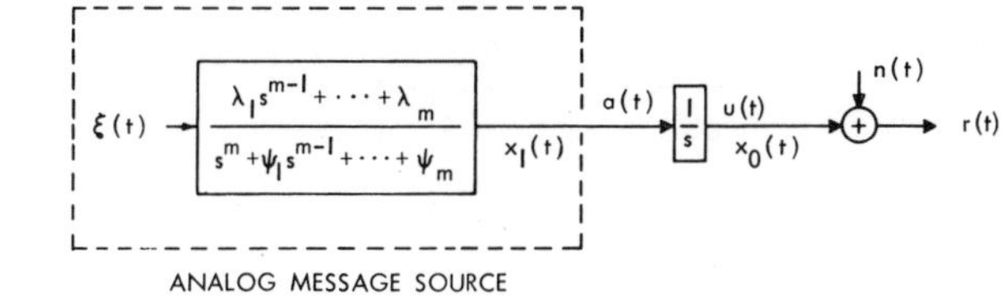

(a)

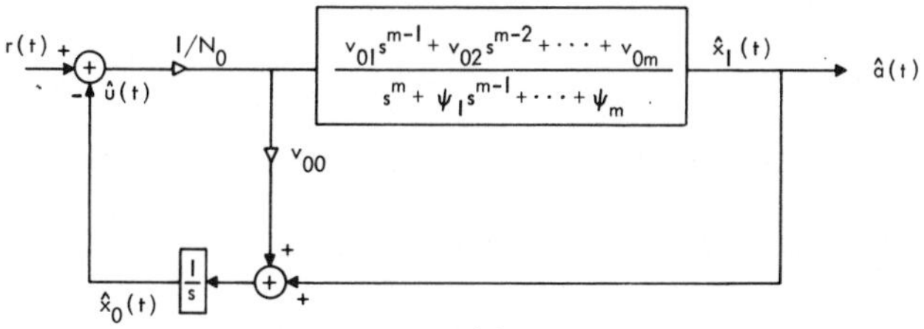

(b)

Figure 5.7(a) An integrated stationary Gaussian message observed in additive white noise. (b) The optimum linear filter for estimating an integrated stationary Gaussian message in additive white noise.

modulator is a particular example of linear filtering that might arise. It will occur again when we consider frequency modulation.

The state vector associated with the analog message source satisfies:

$$\dot{\mathbf{a}}(t) = \mathbf{F}_a \mathbf{a}(t) + \mathbf{G}_a \boldsymbol{\xi}(t) \tag{5.18}$$

where

$$\mathbf{a}(t) = \begin{bmatrix} a_1(t) \\ a_2(t) \\ a_3(t) \\ \cdot \\ \cdot \\ \cdot \\ a_m(t) \end{bmatrix} \qquad \mathbf{F}_a = \begin{bmatrix} -\psi_1 & 1 & 0 & \cdot & \cdot & \cdot & 0 \\ -\psi_2 & 0 & 1 & \cdot & \cdot & \cdot & 0 \\ -\psi_3 & 0 & 0 & 1 & \cdot & \cdot & 0 \\ & & & & \ddots & & \\ \cdot & \cdot & \cdot & & & & \\ \cdot & \cdot & \cdot & & & & 1 \\ -\psi_m & 0 & 0 & \cdot & \cdot & \cdot & 0 \end{bmatrix} \tag{5.19}$$

and

$$G_a = \begin{bmatrix} \lambda_1 \\ \lambda_2 \\ \lambda_3 \\ \cdot \\ \cdot \\ \cdot \\ \lambda_m \end{bmatrix}$$

We assume that $E[\xi(t)\,\xi(u)] = \mathbf{X}\delta(t-u)$ is known. Note that $a(t) = a_1(t)$.

The equation describing the modulator is

$$\dot{u}(t) = a(t) = a_1(t) \tag{5.20}$$

Define $\mathbf{x}$ by

$$\mathbf{x}(t) = \begin{bmatrix} u(t) \\ ---- \\ \mathbf{a}(t) \end{bmatrix} = \begin{bmatrix} x_0(t) \\ x_1(t) \\ x_2(t) \\ \cdot \\ \cdot \\ \cdot \\ x_m(t) \end{bmatrix} \tag{5.21}$$

Then $\mathbf{x}$ satisfies

$$\dot{\mathbf{x}}(t) = \mathbf{F}\mathbf{x}(t) + \mathbf{G}\xi(t) \tag{5.22}$$

where

$$\mathbf{F} = \begin{bmatrix} 0 & 1 & 0 & 0 & \cdot & \cdot & \cdot & 0 \\ 0 & -\psi_1 & 1 & 0 & \cdot & \cdot & \cdot & 0 \\ 0 & -\psi_2 & 0 & 1 & \cdot & \cdot & \cdot & 0 \\ \cdot & \cdot & \cdot & \cdot & & & & \\ \cdot & \cdot & \cdot & \cdot & \cdot & & & \\ \cdot & \cdot & \cdot & \cdot & & \cdot & \cdot & 1 \\ 0 & -\psi_m & 0 & 0 & \cdot & \cdot & \cdot & 0 \end{bmatrix} \qquad \mathbf{G} = \begin{bmatrix} 0 \\ \lambda_1 \\ \lambda_2 \\ \cdot \\ \cdot \\ \cdot \\ \lambda_m \end{bmatrix}$$

Note that $u(t) = x_0(t)$ and $a(t) = x_1(t)$.

The received signal is described by

$$r(t) = u(t) + n(t) = x_0(t) + n(t) \tag{5.23}$$

Thus, $\mathbf{H}(t) = [1 \quad 0 \quad 0 \cdots 0]$.

Under steady-state conditions, the processor and variance equations, Equations 4.3 and 4.4, become

$$\dot{\hat{\mathbf{x}}}(t) = \mathbf{F}\mathbf{x}(t) + \frac{1}{N_0}\begin{bmatrix} v_{00} \\ v_{01} \\ v_{02} \\ \cdot \\ \cdot \\ \cdot \\ v_{0m} \end{bmatrix}[r(t) - \hat{x}_0(t)] \tag{5.24}$$

and

$$\mathbf{0} = \mathbf{FV} + \mathbf{VF}' + \mathbf{X}\mathbf{GG}' - \frac{1}{N_0}\,\mathbf{M} \tag{5.25}$$

where $\mathbf{M}$ is a symmetric $(m + 1) \times (m + 1)$ matrix whose (i, j)-element is $v_{0i}\,v_{0j}$.

The processor equation leads to the realization shown in Figure 5.7b. Once again, we observe that the optimum filter depends only on the first row, or column, of $\mathbf{V}$.

Expressions can be given for v_{00} and v_{11}, the error variances associated with estimating the message a and the integrated message u. The expressions are convenient, because they do not require a determination of the optimum filter or a solution of the variance equation for their evaluation. We shall see later that they are useful in the evaluation of the performance of optimum FM demodulators. The expressions, which are derived in Snyder [44], are

$$v_{00} = N_0 f(0) \tag{5.26}$$

and

$$v_{11} = \frac{N_0}{3}\, f^3(0) + \mathbf{F}(0) \tag{5.27}$$

where f(0) and F(0) are related to $S_a(\omega)$, the spectrum of a, by

$$f(0) = \int_{-\infty}^{\infty} \log \left[1 + \frac{S_a(\omega)}{\omega^2 N_0}\right] \frac{d\omega}{2\pi} \tag{5.28}$$

and

$$F(0) = \int_{-\infty}^{\infty} \omega^2 N_0 \log \left[1 + \frac{S_a(\omega)}{\omega^2 N_0}\right] \frac{d\omega}{2\pi} \tag{5.29}$$

5.2.2.1 *Special case of a one-dimensional message: integral modulation.* As a simple example, consider the one-dimensional

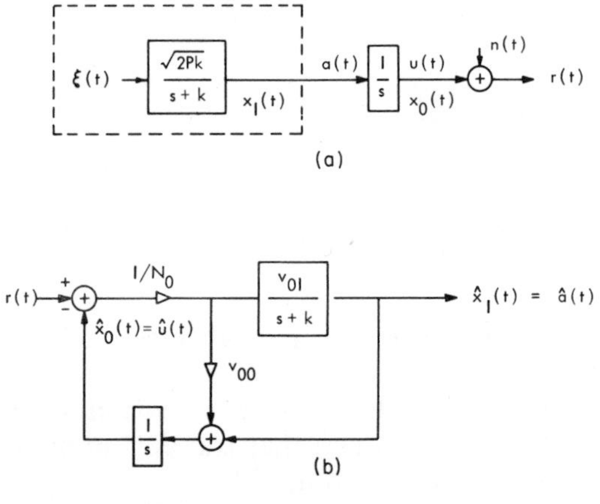

Figure 5.8(a) Integrated one-dimensional Gaussian message observed in additive white noise. (b) The optimum linear filter for estimating an integrated one dimensional Gaussian message observed in additive white noise.

message used in the communication model of Figure 5.8a. For this case, the spectrum of a is $(2\,Pk)/(\omega^2 + k^2)$ watts/cps. We have

$$\mathbf{x}(t) = \begin{bmatrix} x_0(t) \\ x_1(t) \end{bmatrix} \qquad \mathbf{F} = \begin{bmatrix} 0 & 1 \\ 0 & -k \end{bmatrix} \qquad \mathbf{XGG'} = \begin{bmatrix} 0 & 0 \\ 0 & 2Pk \end{bmatrix}$$

The optimum filter is shown in Figure 5.8b. After some straightforward manipulation, the variance equation leads to three equations for the components of **V**

$$\frac{d}{dt} v_{00} = 2v_{01} - \frac{1}{N_0} v_{00}^2 = 0$$

$$\frac{d}{dt} v_{01} = v_{11} - kv_{01} - \frac{1}{N_0} v_{00} v_{01} = 0 \tag{5.30}$$

$$\frac{d}{dt} v_{11} = -2kv_{11} + 2kP - \frac{1}{N_0} v_{01}^2 = 0$$

An equation for v_{00} is obtained by eliminating v_{01} and v_{11} from the second equation

$$\frac{1}{4k^2} \Lambda = \left[\frac{v_{00}}{2kN_0}\right]^4 + 2\left[\frac{v_{00}}{2kN_0}\right]^3 + \left[\frac{v_{00}}{2kN_0}\right]^2$$

This equation becomes

$$\frac{\Lambda}{4k^2} = \left\{\left[\frac{v_{00}}{2kN_0}\right]^2 + \left[\frac{v_{00}}{2kN_0}\right]\right\}^2 \tag{5.31}$$

where $\Lambda = 2P/kN_0$ is the signal-to-noise ratio in the message bandwidth. Solving for v_{00}, we obtain

$$v_{00} = \frac{2N_0\Lambda^{1/2}}{1 + \sqrt{1 + \frac{2}{k}\Lambda^{1/2}}} \tag{5.32}$$

Then v_{01} and v_{11} are easily found to be

$$v_{01} = \frac{2N_0\Lambda}{\left(1 + \sqrt{1 + \frac{2}{k}\Lambda^{1/2}}\right)^2} \tag{5.33}$$

$$v_{11} = P - \frac{2N_0\Lambda^2}{\left(1 + \sqrt{1 + \frac{2}{k}\Lambda^{1/2}}\right)^4 k} \tag{5.34}$$

We have assumed that a is stationary and that $t_0 = -\infty$ in order that steady-state conditions exist. If t_0 is finite, then the only modification to the optimum filter is that v_{00} and v_{01} are time-varying gains rather than constants. We shall see in Chapter 6 that the approach to steady state is rapid compared to the message correlation time. For this reason, the steady-state assumption is usually valid in practice.

Example 5.2.3 Single Message, Double-Sideband Amplitude Modulation with Suppressed Carrier, Additive White Noise Channel

Consider the communication model of Figure 5.9. Here a(t) is a stationary Gaussian message and n(t) is a white Gaussian noise

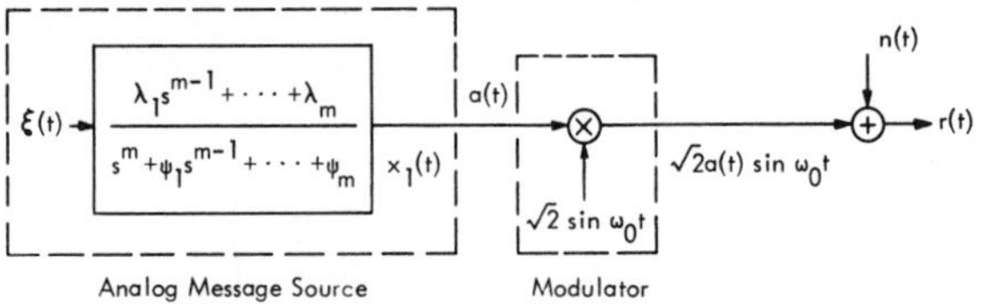

Figure 5.9 Single message transmitted by AM-DSB/SB.

of spectral height N_0 watts/cps. Also, a(t) and n(t) are uncorrelated. The message a(t) amplitude modulates a sinusoidal carrier whose frequency is large compared to significant frequencies of a(t). This is a typical example in which the signal component of r(t) has a bandpass spectrum that is essentially disjoint from that of a(t). The results obtained are similar to those obtained for other linear modulation procedures.

The state vector associated with the message source satisfies

$$\dot{\mathbf{x}}(t) = \mathbf{F}\mathbf{x}(t) + \mathbf{G}\xi(t) \tag{5.35}$$

where $a(t) = x_1(t)$ and where $\mathbf{F}$ and $\mathbf{G}$ are given by

$$\mathbf{F} = \begin{bmatrix} -\psi_1 & 1 & 0 & \cdot & \cdot & \cdot & 0 \\ -\psi_2 & 0 & 1 & 0 & & & \\ -\psi_3 & 0 & 0 & 1 & & & \\ \cdot & & & & & & \\ \cdot & & & & & & \\ \cdot & & & & & & 1 \\ -\psi_m & 0 & 0 & \cdot & \cdot & \cdot & 0 \end{bmatrix} \qquad \mathbf{G} = \begin{bmatrix} \lambda_1 \\ \lambda_2 \\ \lambda_3 \\ \cdot \\ \cdot \\ \cdot \\ \lambda_m \end{bmatrix}$$

We assume that $E[\xi(t)\,\xi(u)] = X\delta(t-u)$ is known.

The received signal is described by

$$r(t) = a(t)\sqrt{2}\,\sin\omega_0 t + n(t)$$
$$= x_1(t)\sqrt{2}\,\sin\omega_0 t + n(t) \tag{5.36}$$

so that $\mathbf{H}(t) = [1 \;\; 0 \;\; 0 \;\; \cdots \;\; 0]\sqrt{2}\,\sin\omega_0 t$.

First we shall examine the variance equation, which is

$$\dot{\mathbf{V}}(t) = \mathbf{F}\mathbf{V}(t) + \mathbf{V}(t)\mathbf{F}' + \mathbf{X}\mathbf{G}\mathbf{G}' - \frac{2}{N_0}\mathbf{M}(t)\,\sin^2\omega_0 t \tag{5.37}$$

where **M** is a symmetric m × m matrix whose (i, j)-element is $v_{1i}(t)\,v_{1j}(t)$. From this equation, it is found that the (i, j)-element of **V** satisfies

$$\dot{v}_{ij}(t) = -\psi_i v_{1j}(t) - \psi_j v_{1i} + v_{i+1,j}(t) + v_{j+1,i}(t) + X\lambda_i\lambda_j$$
$$- \frac{1}{N_0}\, v_{1i}(t)\, v_{1j}(t)\,(1 - \cos 2\omega_0 t) \tag{5.38}$$

Here v_{ij} can be realized as the output of the system diagrammed in Figure 5.10. Inspection of the system indicates that the com-

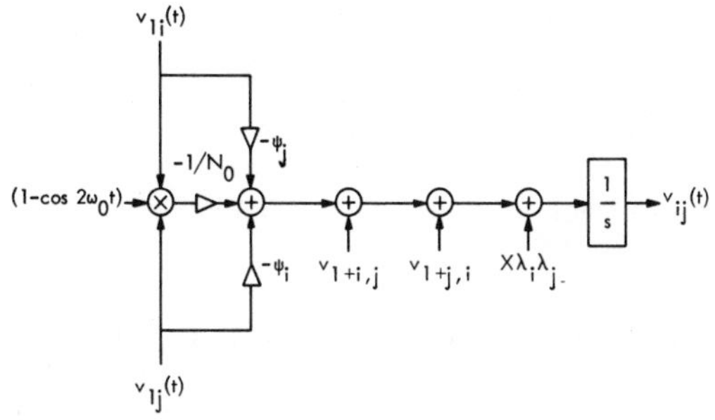

Figure 5.10 A realization for the (i, j)-element of **V**.

ponents of **V** are slowly varying and that the double-frequency signals associated with cos $2\omega_0 t$ have no effect because they will not propagate through the low-pass filter. Consequently, the variance equation can be rewritten as Equation 5.13, the variance equation associated with the no-modulation case of Example 5.2.1. It follows that **V** and, therefore, the estimation performance are the same for both examples.

We now examine the processor equation under the assumption that $t_0 = -\infty$ so that steady-state conditions exist. The processor equation is

$$\dot{\hat{\mathbf{x}}}(t) = \mathbf{F}\hat{\mathbf{x}}(t) + \frac{1}{N_0}\begin{bmatrix} v_{11} \\ v_{12} \\ \cdot \\ \cdot \\ v_{1m} \end{bmatrix} \sqrt{2}\sin\omega_0 t[r(t) - \hat{x}_1(t)\sqrt{2}\sin\omega_0 t] \tag{5.39}$$

The optimum filter is shown in Figure 5.11a. The signal at the output of the upper multiplier is $r(t)\sqrt{2}\sin\omega_0 t - \hat{x}_1(t) + \hat{x}_1(t)\cos 2\omega_0 t$. We observe that $\hat{x}_1(t)$ is slowly varying so that the double-

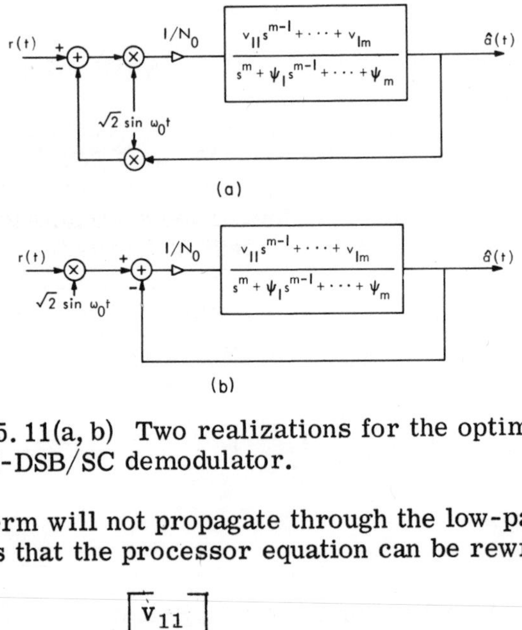

Figure 5.11(a, b) Two realizations for the optimum AM-DSB/SC demodulator.

frequency term will not propagate through the low-pass filter. This implies that the processor equation can be rewritten as

$$\dot{\hat{\mathbf{x}}}(t) = \mathbf{F}\hat{\mathbf{x}}(t) + \frac{1}{N_0}\begin{bmatrix} v_{11} \\ v_{12} \\ \cdot \\ \cdot \\ \cdot \\ v_{1m} \end{bmatrix} [r(t)\sqrt{2}\sin\omega_0 t - \hat{x}_1(t)] \tag{5.40}$$

The modified demodulator is shown in Figure 5.11b.

5.3 APPLICATIONS WHEN x IS GAUSSIAN AND r IS NOT: NONLINEAR MODULATION

For Examples 5.3.1 through 5.3.5, **x** and **r** are described by

$$\dot{\mathbf{x}}(t) = \mathbf{F}(t)\mathbf{x}(t) + \mathbf{G}(t)\xi(t) \tag{5.41}$$

and

$$\dot{\mathbf{y}}(t) = \mathbf{r}(t) = \mathbf{h}[t:\mathbf{x}(t)] + \mathbf{n}(t) \tag{5.42}$$

In general, we shall assume that **F** and **G** are constant matrices and $t_0 = -\infty$ so that **x** is stationary. In this way, the rational polynomial realization of Section 2.1.1 can be used. The nonstationary case can be treated by the simple modification of employing the alternative realization of Section 2.1.1. Equations 4.5 and 4.6 are the processor and variance equations.

Example 5.3.1 Single Message Phase Modulation, Additive White Noise Channel

Consider the communication model shown in Figure 5.12. Here a(t) is a stationary Gaussian message and n(t) is a white Gaussian process of spectral height N_0 watts/cps. The message a(t) phase modulates a sinusoidal carrier whose nominal frequency is large compared to significant frequencies of a(t). We shall assume that the variance of a(t) is unity so that β can be interpreted as the modulation index.

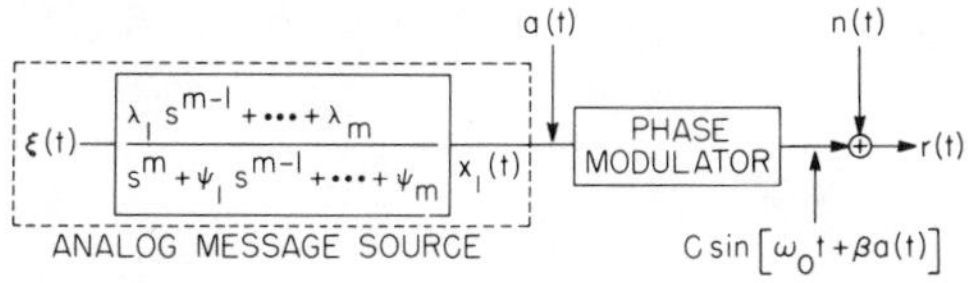

Figure 5.12 A single message transmitted by phase modulation.

The results obtained in this example are typical of those obtained for other memoryless nonlinear modulation schemes in which signals in r(t) associated with the message vary rapidly. A close resemblance exists between the results obtained here and those obtained in the linear modulation cases of Examples 5.2.1 and 5.2.3.

The equations describing the communication model are

$$\dot{\mathbf{x}}(t) = \mathbf{F}\mathbf{x}(t) + \mathbf{G}\xi(t) \qquad a(t) = x_1(t) \tag{5.43}$$

and

$$r(t) = C \sin[\omega_0 t + \beta a(t)] + n(t) \tag{5.44}$$

where **x** is an m-vector and **F** and **G** are the same as defined for Equation 5.35. We assume that $E[\xi(t)\,\xi'(u)] = X\delta(t-u)$ is known. We observe that $\mathbf{h}[t:\mathbf{x}(t)] = C \sin[\omega_0 t + \beta x_1(t)]$, a scalar. Hence,

$$\mathbf{D}[\mathbf{h}(t:\mathbf{x})] = \begin{bmatrix} 1 \\ 0 \\ 0 \\ \cdot \\ \cdot \\ \cdot \\ 0 \end{bmatrix} \beta C \cos[\omega_0 t + \beta x_1(t)] \tag{5.45}$$

After some manipulation, the processor and variance equations, Equations 4.5 and 4.6, become

$$\dot{\mathbf{x}}^*(t) = \mathbf{F}\mathbf{x}^*(t) + \frac{1}{N_0}\begin{bmatrix} v_{11}^*(t) \\ v_{12}^*(t) \\ \cdot \\ \cdot \\ \cdot \\ v_{1m}^*(t) \end{bmatrix} \beta C \cos[\omega_0 t + \beta x_1^*(t)]\{r(t) - C \sin[\omega_0 t + \beta x_1^*(t)]\} \tag{5.46}$$

and

$$\dot{\mathbf{V}}^*(t) = \mathbf{F}\mathbf{V}^*(t) + \mathbf{V}^*(t)\,\mathbf{F}' + X\mathbf{G}\mathbf{G}' - \frac{1}{N_0}\mathbf{M}(t)\,\beta^2 C\{r(t)\sin[\omega_0 t + \beta x_1^*(t)] + C\cos[2\omega_0 t + 2\beta x_1^*(t)]\} \tag{5.47}$$

where **M** is a symmetric m × m matrix whose (i, j)-element is $v_{1i}^*(t)\,v_{1j}^*(t)$. We shall examine the variance equation first. From Equation 5.47, the (i, j)-element of $\mathbf{V}^*$ satisfies

$$\dot{v}_{ij}^*(t) = -\psi_i v_{ij}^*(t) - \psi_j v_{1i}^*(t) + v_{i+1,j}^*(t) + v_{j+1,i}^*(t) + X\lambda_i\lambda_j - \frac{1}{N_0}\beta^2 C v_{1i}^*(t)\,v_{1j}^*(t)\{r(t)\sin[\omega_0 t + \beta x_1^*(t)] + C\cos[2\omega_0 t + 2\beta x_1^*(t)]\} \tag{5.48}$$

Here v^*_{1i} can be realized as the output of the system diagramed in Figure 5.13. Let us now conjecture that the components of $\mathbf{V}^*$ are

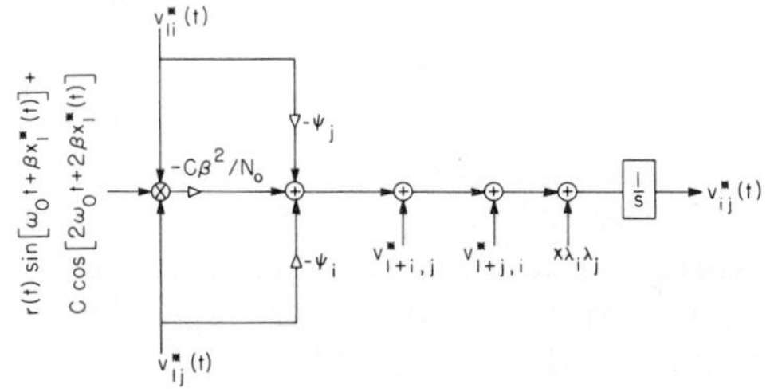

Figure 5.13 A realization for the (i, j)-element of $\mathbf{V}^*$.

slowly varying. We shall find that to a close approximation this is, in fact, true. Then the double-frequency terms associated with $\cos[2\omega_0 t + 2\beta x^*_1(t)]$ will not propagate through the low-pass filtering. Consequently, $\cos[2\omega_0 t + 2\beta x^*_1(t)]$ has negligible effect and can be dropped. The input to the multiplier is then $r(t)\sin[\omega_0 t + \beta x^*_1(t)]$. It is through this term that the variance equation is coupled to both r and $\mathbf{x}^*$. This coupling is a great disadvantage practically, because $\mathbf{V}^*$ and, therefore, the structure of the demodulator, cannot be determined before making observations. For this reason, it is worthwhile to examine $r(t)\sin[\omega_0 t + \beta x^*_1(t)]$ critically so as to obtain any possible simplification. We shall find that a significant simplification is possible.

Observe that the coupling term may be rewritten

$$
\begin{aligned}
r(t)\sin[\omega_0 t + \beta x^*_1(t)] &= n(t)\sin[\omega_0 t + \beta x^*_1(t)] \\
&\quad + C\sin[\omega_0 t + \beta x_1(t)]\sin[\omega_0 t + \beta x^*_1(t)] \\
&= n(t)\sin[\omega_0 t + \beta x^*_1(t)] \\
&\quad + \frac{1}{2}C\cos\beta[x_1(t) - x^*_1(t)] \\
&\quad - \frac{1}{2}C\cos[2\omega_0 t + \beta x_1(t) + \beta x^*_1(t)] \qquad (5.49)
\end{aligned}
$$

Again, the double-frequency term can be disregarded. The second term on the right can be expanded

$$
\frac{1}{2}C\cos\beta[x_1(t) - x^*_1(t)] = \frac{1}{2}C - \frac{1}{4}C\beta^2[x_1(t) - x^*_1(t)]^2 + \cdots \qquad (5.50)
$$

Within the approximation for which the demodulator is optimum, all terms of the expansion except the first can be neglected; the others lead to terms of the order of the sixth moment of the error at the output of the multiplier. Thus, to a good approximation for small error, we have

$$r(t)\ \sin[\omega_0 t + \beta x_1^*(t)] \approx \tfrac{1}{2} C\{1 + \tfrac{2}{C} n(t)\ \sin[\omega_0 t + \beta x_1^*(t)]\}$$

where n is a white process, by which we mean that it has a flat spectrum at least over the frequency range where it has effect. In reality, n has a finite variance given approximately by $N_0 W_c$, where W_c is the channel or receiver input bandwidth. By increasing the channel signal-to-noise ratio $C^2/2N_0 W_c$, it is possible to make the probability of excursions of $[2n(t)]/C$ outside a range around its mean, zero, as small as desired. Since the magnitude of sin $(\cdot)$ is bounded by unity, this implies

$$\tfrac{1}{2}\ C\{1 + \tfrac{2}{C}\ n(t)\ \sin[\omega_0 t + \beta x_1^*(t)]\} \approx \tfrac{1}{2}\ C \tag{5.51}$$

almost always when the signal-to-noise ratio is sufficiently large. We conclude that for large-channel signal-to-noise ratio

$$r(t)\ \sin[\omega_0 t + \beta x_1^*(t)] \approx \frac{1}{2} C \tag{5.52}$$

The approximations have effected an uncoupling of the variance equation from r and $\mathbf{x}^*$, thereby making an important practical simplification in the variance Equation 5.47 that becomes

$$\dot{\mathbf{V}}^*(t) = \mathbf{F}\mathbf{V}^*(t) + \mathbf{V}^*(t)\mathbf{F}' + \mathbf{X}\mathbf{G}\mathbf{G}' - \frac{\beta^2 C^2}{2N_0}\mathbf{M}(t) \tag{5.53}$$

We point out that in getting this result, we have made two signal-to-noise ratio assumptions. The first was made in effect in Chapter 4 with the assumption of small error. In the present application, this would presumably be achieved for a high signal-to-noise ratio in the message or **IF** bandwidth. The second was made to simplify the variance equation to Equation 5.53. This is achieved for a high signal-to-noise ratio in the channel bandwidth. These two bandwidths may or may not be the same. Equation 5.53 is nearly identical to the variance equation associated with the no-modulation case of Example 5.2.1 (see Equation 5.13). Only the noise level must be modified. Also, $\mathbf{V}^*$ can be determined before making any observations, just as in the no-modulation case. It follows from Equation 5.14 that the mean-square estimation error v_{11}^* is given by

$$v_{11}^* = \frac{2N_0}{\beta^2 C^2} \int_{-\infty}^{\infty} \log\left[1 + \frac{\beta^2 C^2}{2N_0}\ S_a(\omega)\right] \frac{d\omega}{2\pi} \tag{5.54}$$

when the signal-to-noise ratio is large. We observe that a useful measure for evaluating the performance of the processor is $\beta^2 v_{11}^*$, the mean-square error in estimating the total phase, $\beta a = \beta x_1$. Viterbi and Cahn [63] have used Equation 5.54 to analyze the above threshold performance of quasi-optimum PM demodulators for the Butterworth class of message spectra.

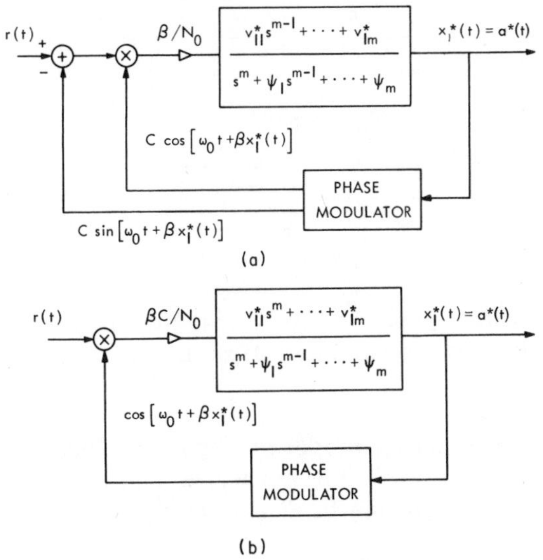

Figure 5.14(a, b) Two realizations for the quasi-optimum PM demodulator.

In the steady state, the processor Equation 5.46 leads to the quasi-optimum PM demodulator of Figure 5.14. It is seen that the subtractive sinusoidal signal results only in double-frequency terms at the output of the multiplier. Since these will not propagate through the filter, the subtractive branch can be discarded. The simplified demodulator is a phase-locked loop as shown in Figure 5.14b. Several interesting properties of the loop filter can be deduced by inspection. These are similar to the properties observed in the linear modulation case of Example 5.2.1. A practical realization of this modulator would employ a voltage-controlled oscillator in the feedback path. These have an additional integration whose effect can be compensated by including an additional differentiation in the forward-loop filter and a post-loop integration to recover $a^*(t)$.

5.3.1.1 *Special case of a one-dimensional message: phase modulation.* As a simple example, consider the one-dimensional mes-

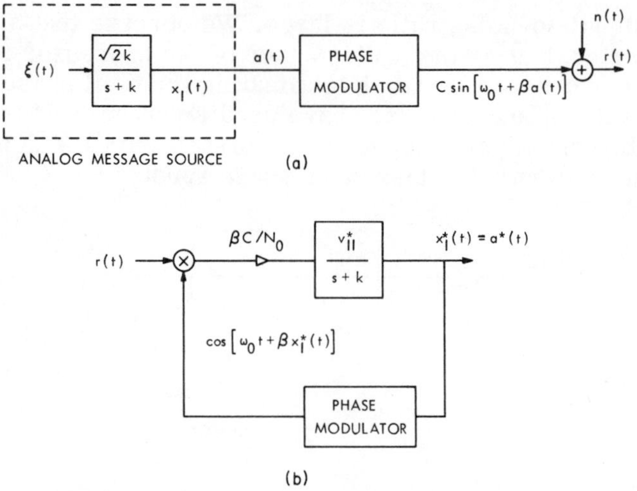

Figure 5.15(a) A one-dimensional message transmitted by PM. (b) The quasi-optimum PM demodulator.

sage in the communication model of Figure 5.15a. For this case, the spectrum of a is $(2k)/(\omega^2 + k^2)$ watts/cps so that a has a variance of unity. Equations 5.43 and 5.44 become

$$\dot{x}_1(t) = -kx_1(t) + \sqrt{2k}\ \xi(t) \tag{5.55}$$

and

$$r(t) = C \sin [\omega_0 t + \beta x_1(t)] + n(t) \tag{5.56}$$

The processor and variance equations, Equations 5.46 and 5.47, become

$$\dot{x}_1^*(t) = -kx_1^*(t) + \frac{\beta C}{N_0} v_{11}(t)\, r(t) \cos [\omega_0 t + \beta x_1^*(t)] \tag{5.57}$$

and

$$\dot{v}_{11}^*(t) = -2kv_{11}^*(t) + 2k - \frac{\beta^2 C^2}{2N_0} v_{11}^{*2}(t) \tag{5.58}$$

where double-frequency terms have been neglected.

The steady-state solution to the variance equation is

$$v_{11}^* = \frac{2}{1 + \sqrt{1 + \beta^2 \Lambda}} \tag{5.59}$$

where $\Lambda = C^2/kN_0$ is the signal-to-noise ratio in the message bandwidth. The optimum demodulator is shown in Figure 5.15b. In Chapter 6, we shall analyze the performance of this demodulator. An explicit expression for the probability density of the steady-state estimation error $\beta[x_1(t) - x_1^*(t)]$ is derived. The expression is valid in all regions of operation including threshold and below.

Example 5.3.2 Single Message, Frequency Modulation, Additive White Noise Channel

Consider the communication model shown in Figure 5.16a. Here a(t) is a stationary Gaussian message and n(t) is a white Gaussian process of spectral height N_0 watts/cps. The message a(t), which is uncorrelated with n(t), frequency modulates a sinusoidal carrier whose nominal frequency is large compared to significant frequencies of a(t). We shall assume that the variance of a(t) is unity. Then d_f is the standard deviation of the frequency from the carrier frequency ω_0.

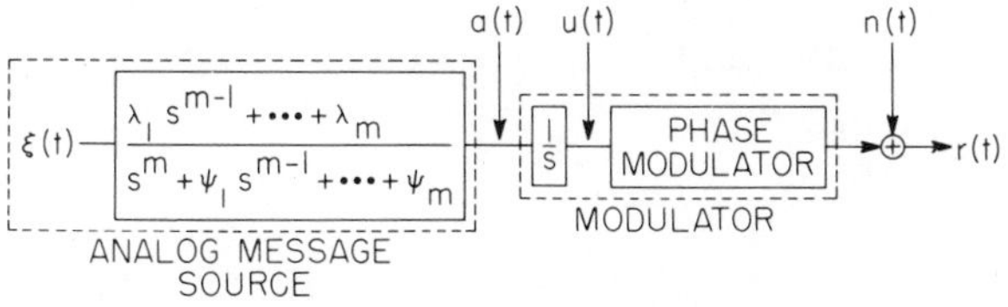

Figure 5.16(a) A single transmitted by frequency modulation.

The results obtained for this example are typical of those obtained for other nonlinear modulation schemes with memory. They bear a close resemblance to the results of the linear, integral modulation case for Example 5.2.2.

The state vector associated with the analog message source satisfies Equation 5.18

$$\dot{\mathbf{a}}(t) = \mathbf{F}_a \mathbf{a}(t) + \mathbf{G}_a \xi(t) \qquad (5.18 \text{ repeated})$$

We assume $E[\xi(t)\,\xi(u)] = X\delta(t-u)$ is known. Note that $a(t) = a_1(t)$ and u(t) is defined by Equation 5.20.

$$\dot{u}(t) = a_1(t) \qquad (5.20 \text{ repeated})$$

If we define **x** by

$$\mathbf{x}(t) = \begin{bmatrix} u(t) \\ --- \\ a(t) \end{bmatrix} = \begin{bmatrix} x_0(t) \\ x_1(t) \\ \cdot \\ \cdot \\ \cdot \\ x_m(t) \end{bmatrix} \qquad \text{(5.21 repeated)}$$

then, as before, **x** satisfies

$$\dot{\mathbf{x}}(t) = \mathbf{Fx} + \mathbf{G}\xi(t) \qquad \text{(5.22 repeated)}$$

Note that $u(t) = x_0(t)$ and $a(t) = x_1(t)$.

The received signal is described by

$$\begin{aligned} r(t) &= C \sin\left[\omega_0 t + d_f \int_{t_0}^{t} a(\tau)\, d\tau\right] + n(t) \\ &= C \sin\left[\omega_0 t + d_f x_0(t)\right] + n(t) \end{aligned} \qquad (5.60)$$

so that $\mathbf{h}[t:\mathbf{x}(t)] = C \sin[\omega_0 t + d_f x_0(t)]$ and

$$\mathbf{D}[\mathbf{h}(t:\mathbf{x})] = \begin{bmatrix} 1 \\ 0 \\ 0 \\ \cdot \\ \cdot \\ \cdot \\ 0 \end{bmatrix} d_f C \cos\left[\omega_0 t + d_f x_0(t)\right] \qquad (5.61)$$

After some manipulation, the variance and processor equations, Equations 4.5 and 4.6, become

$$\dot{\mathbf{x}}^*(t) = \mathbf{Fx}^*(t) + \frac{1}{N_0} \begin{bmatrix} v^*_{00}(t) \\ v^*_{01}(t) \\ \cdot \\ \cdot \\ \cdot \\ v^*_{0m}(t) \end{bmatrix} d_f C \cos\left[\omega_0 t + d_f x^*_0(t)\right] \times \left\{r(t) - C \sin\left[\omega_0 t + d_f x^*_0(t)\right]\right\} \qquad (5.62)$$

and

$$\dot{\mathbf{V}}^*(t) = \mathbf{F}\mathbf{V}^*(t) + \mathbf{V}^*(t)\mathbf{F}' + \mathbf{X}\mathbf{G}\mathbf{G}'$$

$$- \frac{1}{N_0} \mathbf{M}(t) d_f^2 C \{r(t) \sin [\omega_0 t + d_f x_0^*(t)]$$

$$+ C \cos [2\omega_0 t + 2d_f x_0^*(t)]\} \quad (5.63)$$

where $\mathbf{M}$ is a symmetric $(m + 1) \times (m + 1)$ matrix whose (i, j)-element is $v_{0i}^*(t)\, v_{0j}^*(t)$. We observe that Equation 5.63 is equivalent to Equation 5.47, the variance equation for the PM case. Therefore, the arguments leading to the simplified variance equation, Equation 5.53, carry over and Equation 5.63 becomes

$$\dot{\mathbf{V}}^*(t) = \mathbf{F}\mathbf{V}^*(t) + \mathbf{V}^*(t)\mathbf{F}' + \mathbf{X}\mathbf{G}\mathbf{G}' - \frac{d_f^2 C^2}{2N_0} \mathbf{M}(t) \quad (5.64)$$

In the steady state and with a change in noise level, Equation 5.64 is identical to Equation 5.25, the variance equation for the linear integral-modulation case. Using this observation, it follows from Equations 5.26 through 5.29 that the steady-state mean-square errors in estimating $x_0(t)$, the integrated message, and $x_1(t)$, the message, are given by

$$v_{00}^* = \frac{2N_0}{d_f^2 C^2} f(0) \quad (5.65)$$

and

$$v_{11}^* = \frac{2N_0}{3 d_f^2 C^2} f^3(0) + F(0) \quad (5.66)$$

where

$$f(0) = \int_{-\infty}^{\infty} \log \left[1 + \frac{d_f^2 C^2}{2N_0} \frac{S_a(\omega)}{\omega^2}\right] \frac{d\omega}{2\pi} \quad (5.67a)$$

and

$$F(0) = \int_{-\infty}^{\infty} \frac{2N_0}{d_f^2 C^2}\, \omega^2 \log \left[1 + \frac{d_f^2 C^2}{2N_0} \frac{S_a(\omega)}{\omega^2}\right] \frac{d\omega}{2\pi} \quad (5.67b)$$

A useful measure for evaluating the performance of the FM demodulator is $d_f{}^2 v^*_{00}$, the mean-square error in estimating the total phase $d_f x_0(t)$. Equations 5.65 and 5.66 are important, because with them, the performance can be studied without determining the structure of the demodulator. The equations have been evaluated numerically for the Butterworth class of message spectra. The results are presented in Chapter 6.

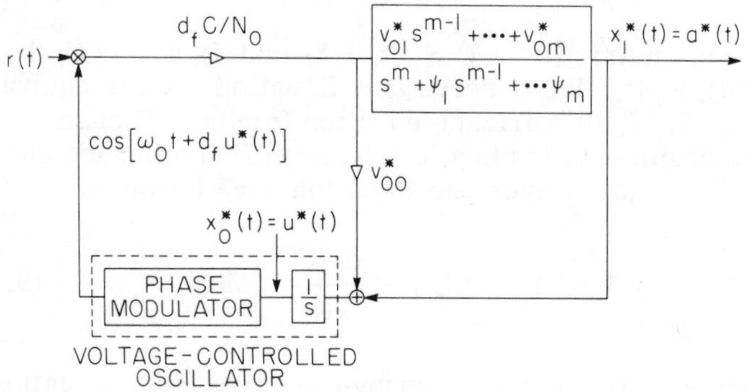

Figure 5.16(b) The quasi-optimum FM demodulator.

In the steady state, the processor equation, Equation 5.62, leads to the quasi-optimum FM demodulator of Figure 5.16b. (The subtractive sinusoidal term of Equation 5.62 has been omitted, because it has no effect.) This demodulator can be placed in the form of a phase-locked loop, which is optimum for estimating u, and a realizable post-loop filter, whose output is a*. It is this last structure that arises most naturally with Lehan and Parks' [35] approach and is probably more familiar. The demodulator of Figure 5.16b has the advantage of requiring one less filter.

5.3.2.1 *Special case of a one-dimensional message: frequency modulation.* As a simple example, consider the one-dimensional message in the communication model of Figure 5.17a. For this case, the spectrum of a is $(2k)/(\omega^2 + k^2)$ watts/cps so that a(t) has a variance of unity. The processor and variance equations, Equations 5.62 and 5.63, become

$$\dot{\mathbf{x}}^*(t) = \mathbf{F}\mathbf{x}^*(t) + \frac{1}{N_0}\begin{bmatrix} v^*_{00}(t) \\ v^*_{01}(t) \end{bmatrix} d_f C r(t) \cos[\omega_0 t + d_f x^*_0(t)] \qquad (5.68)$$

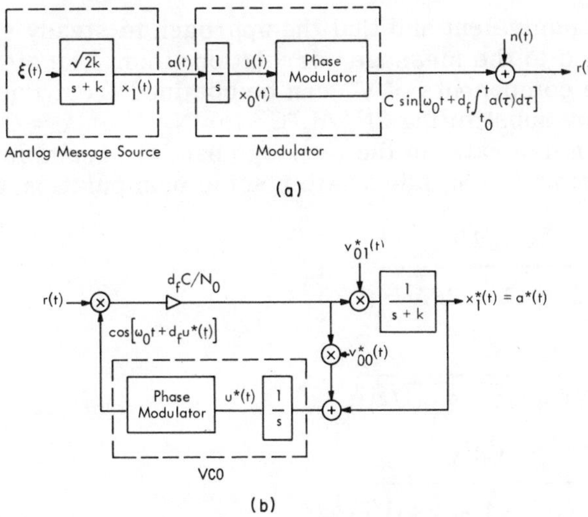

Figure 5.17(a) A one-dimensional message transmitted by FM. (b) The quasi-optimum FM demodulator in the transient case.

and

$$\dot{\mathbf{V}}^*(t) = \mathbf{F}\mathbf{V}^*(t) + \mathbf{V}^*(t)\mathbf{F}' + \mathbf{X}\mathbf{G}\mathbf{G}'$$

$$- \frac{1}{N_0}\begin{bmatrix} v_{00}^* v_{00}^* & v_{00}^* v_{01}^* \\ v_{01}^* v_{00}^* & v_{01}^* v_{01}^* \end{bmatrix} d_f^2 C r(t) \sin\left[\omega_0 t + d_f x_0^*(t)\right] \quad (5.69)$$

where double-frequency terms have been neglected. The simplified variance equation, Equation 5.64, becomes

$$\dot{\mathbf{V}}^*(t) = \mathbf{F}\mathbf{V}^*(t) + \mathbf{V}^*(t)\mathbf{F}' + \mathbf{X}\mathbf{G}\mathbf{G}'$$

$$- \frac{d_f^2 C^2}{2N_0}\begin{bmatrix} v_{00}^* v_{00}^* & v_{00}^* v_{01}^* \\ v_{01}^* v_{00}^* & v_{01}^* v_{01}^* \end{bmatrix} \quad (5.70)$$

The quasi-optimum FM demodulator for the one-dimensional message is shown in Figure 5.17b. In Chapter 6, we shall present the results of a computer simulation of this demodulator. For the simulation, v_{00}^* and v_{01}^* were generated by both Equations 5.69 and 5.70. The results of the simulation indicate that the variance equations are equivalent and that the approach to steady state is rapid compared to the message correlation time. The steady-state values for the components of $\mathbf{V}^*$ can be obtained from Equations 5.32 to 5.34 by substituting $2N_0/d_f^2C^2$ for N_0. Let $\Lambda = C^2/kN_0$, the signal-to-noise ratio in the message bandwidth, and let $\beta = d_f/k$, the modulation index. After some manipulation, we obtain

$$d_f^2 v_{00}^* = \frac{4\beta\Lambda^{-1/2}}{1 + \sqrt{1 + 2\beta\Lambda^{1/2}}} \tag{5.71}$$

$$d_f\, v_{01}^* = \frac{4\beta}{(1 + \sqrt{1 + 2\beta\Lambda^{1/2}})^2} \tag{5.72}$$

$$v_{11}^* = 1 - \frac{4\beta^2\Lambda}{(1 + \sqrt{1 + 2\beta\Lambda^{1/2}})^4} \tag{5.73}$$

Example 5.3.3 Single Message, Frequency Modulation, c Diversity Channels

The diversity communication system of Figure 5.18 consists of a single, stationary Gaussian message transmitted by c fre-

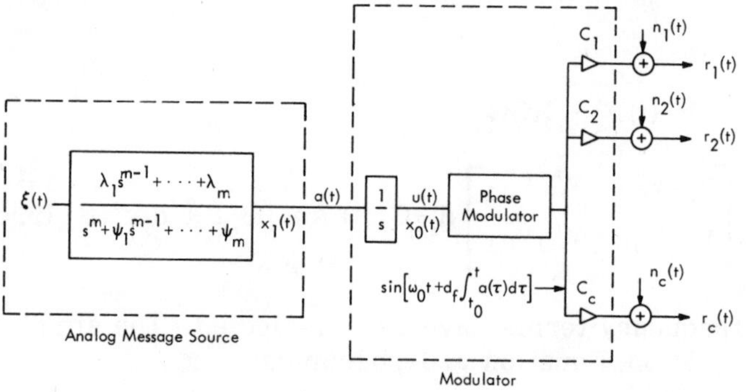

Figure 5.18 FM diversity communication system.

quency-modulated signals, each differing only in amplitude, over c links. Each link has additive observation noise. The model can also be interpreted as representing a fixed known multipath channel with different gains associated with each path. Other diversity modulation schemes, such as frequency-diversity FM, are treated in a fashion parallel to this example.

We shall use the representation for FM of Example 5.3.2 so that $\mathbf{x}$ is given by Equation 5.22.

Let the additive disturbances be independent, and white Gaussian. **N** is then of the form

$$\mathbf{N} = \begin{bmatrix} N_1 & & & & & \\ & N_2 & & 0 & & \\ & & \cdot & & & \\ & & & \cdot & & \\ & 0 & & & \cdot & \\ & & & & & N_c \end{bmatrix} \tag{5.74}$$

The received signal is

$$\mathbf{r}(t) = \begin{bmatrix} C_1 \\ C_2 \\ C_3 \\ \cdot \\ \cdot \\ \cdot \\ C_c \end{bmatrix} \sin\left[\omega_0 t + d_f x_0(t)\right] + \mathbf{n}(t) \tag{5.75}$$

Also, $D[\mathbf{h}(t:\mathbf{x})]$ is given by

$$D[\mathbf{h}(t:\mathbf{x})] = \begin{bmatrix} C_1 & C_2 & C_3 & \cdots & C_c \\ 0 & 0 & 0 & & 0 \\ \cdot & & & & \\ \cdot & & & & \\ \cdot & & & & \\ 0 & 0 & 0 & & 0 \end{bmatrix} d_f \cos\left[\omega_0 t + d_f x_0(t)\right] \tag{5.76}$$

After some manipulation, the processor equation, Equation 4.5, becomes

$$\dot{\mathbf{x}}^*(t) = \mathbf{F}\mathbf{x}^*(t) + \begin{bmatrix} v_{00}(t) \\ v_{01}(t) \\ v_{02}(t) \\ \cdot \\ \cdot \\ \cdot \\ v_{0m}(t) \end{bmatrix} \left[\sum_{i=1}^{c} \frac{C_i}{N_i} r_i(t)\right] d_f \cos\left[\omega_0 t + d_f x_0^*(t)\right] \tag{5.77}$$

when double-frequency terms are neglected.

The variance equation reduces to a linear equivalent variance equation just as in the PM and FM examples considered previously.

The quasi-optimum diversity FM demodulator, in the steady state, is shown in Figure 5.19. It consists of a maximal-ratio

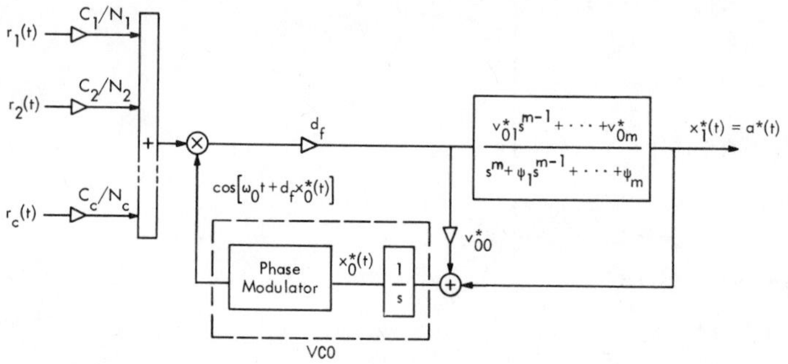

Figure 5.19 Quasi-optimum demodulator for a FM diversity communication system.

combiner followed by a scalar FM demodulator. This result is the same as obtained by Van Trees [56] in connection with the multilink transmission of phase-modulated signals.

Example 5.3.4 Single Message, Frequency Modulation, Rayleigh Channel

A communication model for a frequency modulated sinusoid transmitted over a Rayleigh channel is shown in Figure 5.20. The transmitted signal

$$C \sin [\omega_0 t + d_f u(t)] = C \sin [\omega_0 t + d_f \int_{t_0}^{t} a(\mu)\, d\mu] \qquad (5.78)$$

is frequency modulated by a message process a. The received signal

$$r(t) = b_1(t)\, C \sin [\omega_0 t + d_f u(t)] + b_2(t)\, C \cos [\omega_0 t + d_f u(t)] + n(t) \qquad (5.79)$$

contains in-phase and quadrature versions of the transmitted signal, each amplitude modulated independently by a fading process. Here b_1, b_2, a, and n are uncorrelated Gaussian processes. The fading processes b_1 and b_2 have identical power spectral densities, and n is white with a spectral height of N_0 watts/cps.

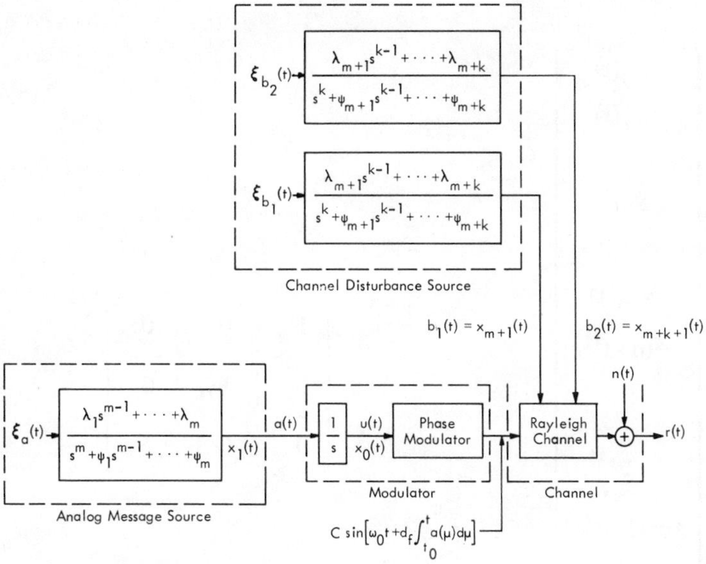

Figure 5.20 A single FM signal transmitted via a Rayleigh channel.

Let ρ and θ by defined by

$$\rho^2(t) = b_1^2(t) + b_2^2(t) \tag{5.80}$$

and

$$\theta(t) = \tan^{-1}\left[\frac{b_2(t)}{b_1(t)}\right] \qquad 0 \leqslant \theta < 2\pi \tag{5.81}$$

Then ρ is Rayleigh distributed and, at the same instant, independent of θ which is uniformly distributed between 0 and 2π. The received signal can be expressed in terms of the envelope ρ and phase θ processes by

$$r(t) = \rho(t)C \sin\left[\omega_0 t + d_f \int_{t_0}^{t} a(\mu)d\mu + \theta(t)\right] + n(t) \tag{5.82}$$

The $(m + 2k + 1)$-dimensional state vector $\mathbf{x}$, characterizing the message, modulator, and channel, satisfies

$$\dot{\mathbf{x}}(t) = \mathbf{F}\mathbf{x}(t) + \mathbf{G}\xi(t) \tag{5.83}$$

where

$$\mathbf{x}(t) = \begin{bmatrix} x_0(t) \\ x_1(t) \\ \cdot \\ \cdot \\ \cdot \\ x_m(t) \\ x_{m+1}(t) \\ \cdot \\ \cdot \\ \cdot \\ x_{m+k+1}(t) \\ \cdot \\ \cdot \\ \cdot \\ x_{m+2k}(t) \end{bmatrix} \qquad \mathbf{F} = \left[\begin{array}{c|c|c} \mathbf{F}_a & 0 & 0 \\ \hline 0 & \mathbf{F}_b & 0 \\ \hline 0 & 0 & \mathbf{F}_b \end{array}\right]$$

$$\mathbf{G} = \left[\begin{array}{c|c|c} \mathbf{G}_a & 0 & 0 \\ \hline 0 & \mathbf{G}_b & 0 \\ \hline 0 & 0 & \mathbf{G}_b \end{array}\right] \qquad \xi(t) = \begin{bmatrix} \xi_a(t) \\ \xi_{b_1}(t) \\ \xi_{b_2}(t) \end{bmatrix}$$

Note from Figure 5.20 that $u = x_0$, $a = x_1$, $b_1 = x_{m+1}$, and $b_2 = x_{m+k+1}$. The matrices $\mathbf{F}_a$ and $\mathbf{G}_a$ are identical to the matrices $\mathbf{F}$ and $\mathbf{G}$ associated with Equation 5.22 of the linear integral modulation example. The remaining matrices $\mathbf{F}_b$ and $\mathbf{G}_b$ are given by

$$\mathbf{F}_b = \begin{bmatrix} -\psi_{m+1} & 1 & 0 & \cdot & \cdot & \cdot & 0 \\ -\psi_{m+2} & 0 & 1 & \cdot & \cdot & \cdot & 0 \\ \cdot & \cdot & \cdot & \cdot & & & \\ \cdot & \cdot & \cdot & & \cdot & & \\ \cdot & \cdot & \cdot & & & \cdot & 1 \\ -\psi_{m+k} & 0 & 0 & \cdot & \cdot & \cdot & 0 \end{bmatrix} \qquad \mathbf{G}_b = \begin{bmatrix} \lambda_{m+1} \\ \lambda_{m+2} \\ \cdot \\ \cdot \\ \cdot \\ \lambda_{m+k} \end{bmatrix}$$

From Equation 5.79 or Figure 5.20, we see that h is given by

$$h[t:\mathbf{x}(t)] = x_{m+1}(t)C\sin[\omega_0 t + d_f x_0(t)] + x_{m+k+1}(t)C\cos[\omega_0 t + d_f x_0(t)] \quad (5.84)$$

The estimated message and, if desired, the estimated channel processes are obtained from the estimated state $\mathbf{x}^*$ that satisfies the processor equation, Equation 4.5,

$$\dot{\mathbf{x}}^*(t) = \mathbf{F}\mathbf{x}^*(t) + \frac{1}{N_0}\mathbf{V}^*(t)\mathbf{D}[h(t:\mathbf{x}^*)]\{r(t) - h[t:\mathbf{x}^*(t)]\} \quad (5.85)$$

where the approximate error covariance matrix $\mathbf{V}^*$ satisfies the variance equation, Equation 4.6

$$\mathbf{V}^*(t) = \mathbf{F}\mathbf{V}^*(t) + \mathbf{V}^*(t)\mathbf{F}' + \mathbf{G}\mathbf{X}\mathbf{G}' + \frac{1}{N_0}\mathbf{V}^*(t)\mathbf{D}[\mathbf{D}[h(t:\mathbf{x}^*)]\{r(t) - h(t:\mathbf{x}^*)\}]\mathbf{V}^*(t) \quad (5.86)$$

and $\mathbf{D}[h(t:\mathbf{x}^*)]$ is the $(m + 2k + 1)$-vector

$$C\begin{bmatrix} x_{m+1}(t)d_f\cos[\omega_0 t + d_f x_0(t)] - x_{m+k+1}(t)d_f\sin[\omega_0 t + d_f x_0(t)] \\ 0 \\ \cdot \\ \cdot \\ \cdot \\ \sin[\omega_0 t + d_f x_0(t)] \\ 0 \\ \cdot \\ \cdot \\ \cdot \\ \cos[\omega_0 t + d_f x_0(t)] \\ 0 \\ \cdot \\ \cdot \\ \cdot \\ 0 \end{bmatrix} \begin{matrix} (\text{row } 0) \\ \\ \\ \\ \\ (\text{row } m+1) \\ \\ \\ \\ \\ (\text{row } m+1+k) \\ \\ \\ \\ \\ \\ \end{matrix}$$

The variance equation cannot be simplified in this case as it could in the absence of fading, because the sequence of steps leading to the approximation of $r(t)\sin[\omega_0 t + d_f x_0^*(t)]$ in Equation 5.52 results now in a function of the unknown channel fading processes and not a constant. Consequently, the variance equation apparently cannot be uncoupled from r or from $\mathbf{x}^*$. This implies that the resulting receiver structure is more complicated than might at first be anticipated. Nevertheless, the receiver can be realized, because all the terms in Equations 5.85 and 5.86 are either known or can

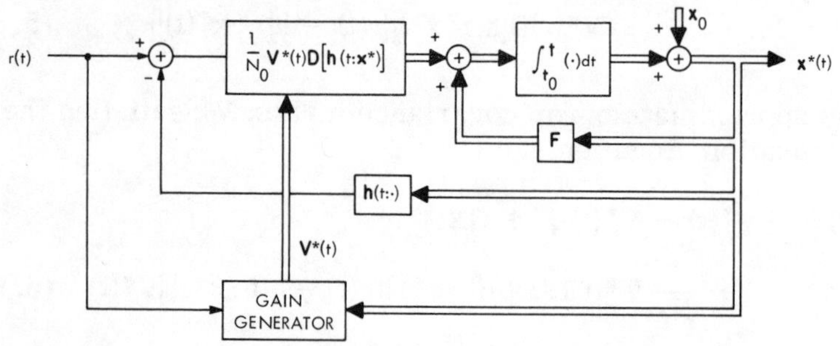

Figure 5.21 Vector block diagram of a quasi-optimum demodulator for FM and a Rayleigh channel.

be generated as data arrive. A general vector block diagram of the receiver is shown in Figure 5.21.

Observe that $h[t:\mathbf{x}^*(t)]$ and the first element of $\mathbf{D}[h(t:\mathbf{x}^*)]$ can be written as

$$Cd_f\sqrt{x_{m+1}^{*2}(t) + x_{m+k+1}^{*2}(t)}\ \sin\left\{\omega_0 t + d_f x_0^*(t) + \tan^{-1}\left[\frac{x_{m+k+1}^*(t)}{x_{m+1}^*(t)}\right]\right\}$$

Consequently, if we define ρ^* and θ^* by

$$\rho^{*2}(t) = x_{m+1}^{*2}(t) + x_{m+k+1}^{*2}(t) \tag{5.87}$$

and

$$\theta^*(t) = \tan^{-1}\left[\frac{x_{m+k+1}^*(t)}{x_{m+1}^*(t)}\right] \qquad 0 \leq \theta^* < 2\pi \tag{5.88}$$

then the receiver can be interpreted as estimating the amplitude and phase of the Rayleigh faded signal defined by Equation 5.82.†

† It should be noted that ρ^* and θ^* are not the minimum-mean-square error estimates of ρ and θ.

It may at first seem surprising to attempt to estimate θ which is uniformly distributed and independent of ρ at the same instant. However, recall that ρ and θ are not independent processes (see Davenport and Root [12], p. 161) and, furthermore, θ is generally a slowly varying correlated process. Thus, once the receiver is synchronized (i.e., $\theta - \theta^*$ is small), θ can presumably be tracked with relatively small rms error.

Example 5.3.5 Single Message, Phase Modulation, Random Phase Channel

The purpose of this example is to indicate that nonmultiplicative channel disturbances fall within the scope of the approach and the procedure for treating a specific instance of such a disturbance that arises in practice.

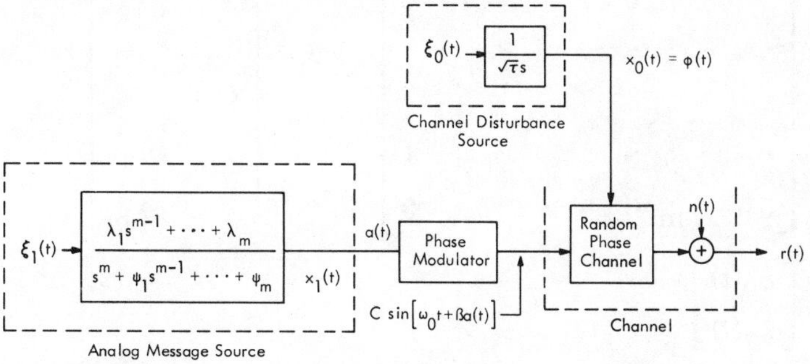

Figure 5.22 Phase modulation and a random phase channel (oscillator instability).

The communication model of Figure 5.22 represents the transmission of a phase-modulated signal over a channel that introduces a random phase disturbance. The model can be interpreted as representing a phase-modulation system with an unstable oscillator. The phase disturbance φ is assumed to be a Wiener process with a variance parameter $1/\tau$ where τ is the coherence time of the oscillator. It is the interval during which the oscillator accumulates one radian (rms) of phase drift compared to an ideal stable oscillator and represents approximately the duration over which a coherent demodulator (that neglects φ) can operate usefully. Edson [18] and Develet [15] have used such a process to characterize oscillator instabilities.

Let $\mathbf{x}$ be an $(m + 1)$-vector defined by

$$\dot{\mathbf{x}}(t) = \mathbf{F}\mathbf{x}(t) + \mathbf{G}\boldsymbol{\xi}(t) \tag{5.89}$$

where

$$\mathbf{x}(t) = \begin{bmatrix} \varphi(t) \\ \text{- - -} \\ a(t) \end{bmatrix} = \begin{bmatrix} x_0(t) \\ x_1(t) \\ \cdot \\ \cdot \\ \cdot \\ x_{m+1}(t) \end{bmatrix}$$

$$\mathbf{F} = \begin{bmatrix} 0 & 0 & 0 & 0 & \cdot & \cdot & 0 \\ 0 & -\psi_1 & 1 & 0 & \cdot & \cdot & 0 \\ 0 & -\psi_2 & 0 & 1 & \cdot & \cdot & 0 \\ \cdot & \cdot & \cdot & & \cdot & & \cdot \\ \cdot & \cdot & \cdot & & & \cdot & \cdot \\ \cdot & \cdot & \cdot & & & & 1 \\ 0 & -\psi_m & 0 & \cdot & \cdot & \cdot & 0 \end{bmatrix} \qquad \mathbf{G} = \left[\begin{array}{c|c} \tau^{-1/2} & 0 \\ \hline & \lambda_1 \\ & \lambda_2 \\ & \cdot \\ 0 & \cdot \\ & \cdot \\ & \lambda_m \end{array}\right]$$

$$\xi(t) = \begin{bmatrix} \xi_0(t) \\ \xi_1(t) \end{bmatrix}$$

Note that $\varphi(t) = x_0(t)$ and $a(t) = x_1(t)$.

The received signal is given by

$$r(t) = C \sin [\omega_0 t + \beta a(t) + \varphi(t)] + n(t) \tag{5.90}$$

so that

$$h[t:\mathbf{x}(t)] = C \sin [\omega_0 t + \beta x_1(t) + x_0(t)] \tag{5.91}$$

Then

$$\mathbf{D}[h(t:\mathbf{x})] = \begin{bmatrix} 1 \\ \beta \\ 0 \\ \cdot \\ \cdot \\ \cdot \\ 0 \end{bmatrix} C \cos [\omega_0 t + \beta x_1(t) + x_0(t)] \tag{5.92}$$

As in the case of the pure phase-modulation example, Example 5.3.1, the variance equation, Equation 4.6, becomes uncoupled from r(t) and $\mathbf{x}^*$ when only significant terms are retained.

From the processor equation, Equation 4.5, we obtain

$$\dot{\mathbf{x}}^*(t) = \mathbf{F}\mathbf{x}^*(t) + \frac{1}{N_0}\begin{bmatrix} v_{00}^*(t) + \beta v_{10}^*(t) \\ v_{01}^*(t) + \beta v_{11}^*(t) \\ \cdot \\ \cdot \\ \cdot \\ v_{0m}^*(t) + \beta v_{1m}^*(t) \end{bmatrix} Cr(t)\cos[\omega_0 t + \beta x_1^*(t) + x_0^*(t)] \quad (5.93)$$

where double-frequency terms have been neglected. It is observed that the equation depends only on 2 columns of the error-covariance matrix $\mathbf{V}^*$. The quasi-optimum demodulator under steady-state conditions is shown in Figure 5.23.

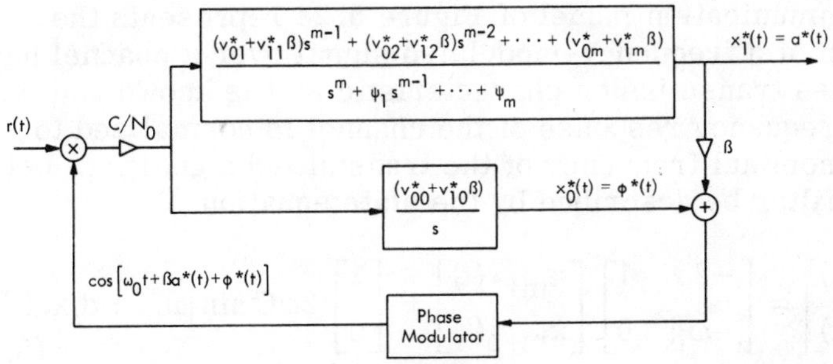

Figure 5.23 Quasi-optimum demodulator for estimating a phase-modulated signal in a random phase channel.

5.4 APPLICATIONS WHEN NEITHER x NOR r IS GAUSSIAN

For Examples 5.4.1 to 5.4.3, **x** and **r** are described by

$$\dot{\mathbf{x}}(t) = \mathbf{f}[t:\mathbf{x}(t)] + \mathbf{G}(t)\,\boldsymbol{\xi}(t) \quad (5.94)$$

and

$$\mathbf{r}(t) = \mathbf{h}[t:\mathbf{x}(t)] + \mathbf{n}(t) \quad (5.95)$$

Equations 4.1 and 4.2 are the variance and processor equations, respectively.

Example 5.4.1 Single Message, Frequency Modulation, Fixed Channel with Memory

The purpose of this example is to indicate how fixed channels with memory are treated. The same procedure is also followed for modulation schemes with linear filtering after a nonlinear transformation.

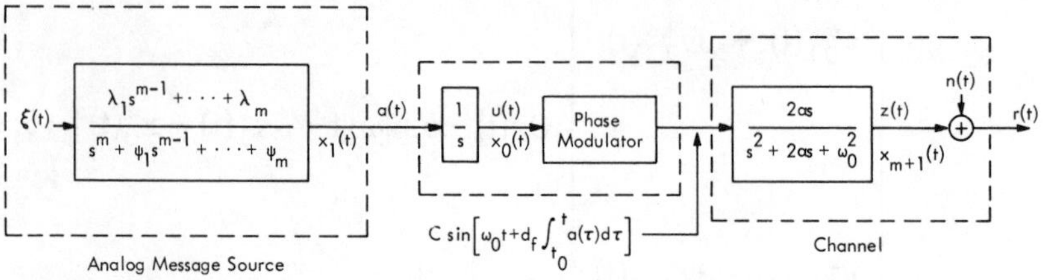

Figure 5.24 FM transmitted through a fixed channel with memory.

The communication model of Figure 5.24 represents the transmission of a frequency-modulated signal over a channel having a bandpass transmission characteristic that is known and fixed. The frequency response of the channel is normalized to unity at the nominal frequency of the transmitted signal ω_0. Let the channel filter be described by the state equation

$$\frac{d}{dt}\begin{bmatrix} x_{m+1}(t) \\ x_{m+2}(t) \end{bmatrix} = \begin{bmatrix} -2\alpha & 1 \\ -\omega_0^2 & 0 \end{bmatrix}\begin{bmatrix} x_{m+1}(t) \\ x_{m+2}(t) \end{bmatrix} + \begin{bmatrix} 1 \\ 0 \end{bmatrix} 2\alpha C \sin[\omega_0 t + d_f x_0(t)] \tag{5.96}$$

where $z(t) = x_{m+1}(t)$ is the response of the filter to the channel input $C \sin[\omega_0 t + d_f x_0(t)]$. A time-variant channel response can be treated by simply modifying the filter state equation.

As in the pure FM example, Example 5.3.2, a and u are described by

$$\frac{d}{dt}\begin{bmatrix} x_0(t) \\ x_1(t) \\ \cdot \\ \cdot \\ \cdot \\ x_m(t) \end{bmatrix} = \mathbf{F}\begin{bmatrix} x_0(t) \\ x_1(t) \\ \cdot \\ \cdot \\ \cdot \\ x_m(t) \end{bmatrix} + \begin{bmatrix} 0 \\ \lambda_1 \\ \cdot \\ \cdot \\ \cdot \\ \lambda_m \end{bmatrix} \xi(t) \tag{5.97}$$

where **F** is the same as defined for Equation 5.22 of the linear integral-modulation case.

The (m + 3)-vector **x**, obtained by adjoining the two-dimensional channel state vector with the (m + 1)-dimensional message and modulator state vector, satisfies

$$\dot{\mathbf{x}}(t) = \mathbf{f}[t:\mathbf{x}(t)] + \mathbf{G}\xi(t) \tag{5.98}$$

where

$$\mathbf{x}(t) = \begin{bmatrix} x_0(t) \\ x_1(t) \\ \cdot \\ \cdot \\ \cdot \\ x_m(t) \\ x_{m+2}(t) \\ x_{m+2}(t) \end{bmatrix} \qquad \mathbf{G} = \begin{bmatrix} 0 \\ \lambda_1 \\ \cdot \\ \cdot \\ \cdot \\ \lambda_m \\ 0 \\ 0 \end{bmatrix}$$

Note that $u(t) = x_0(t)$, $a(t) = x_1(t)$, and $z(t) = x_{m+1}(t)$. The vector, **f** is given by

$$\mathbf{f}[t:\mathbf{x}(t)] = \left[\begin{array}{c|cc} \mathbf{F} & \multicolumn{2}{c}{0} \\ \hline & -2\alpha & 1 \\ 0 & & \\ & -\omega_0^2 & 0 \end{array}\right] \mathbf{x}(t) + \begin{bmatrix} 0 \\ 0 \\ \cdot \\ \cdot \\ \cdot \\ 0 \\ 1 \\ 0 \end{bmatrix} 2\alpha C \sin[\omega_0 t + d_f x_0(t)] \tag{5.99}$$

It is observed that **f** is composed of a linear and a nonlinear transformation of **x**. Let $\mathbf{F}_l$ denote the matrix associated with the linear transformation. Then,

$$D[\mathbf{f}(t:\mathbf{x})] = \mathbf{F}_l' + \begin{bmatrix} 0 & 0 & \cdot & \cdot & \cdot & 0 & 1 & 0 \\ 0 & 0 & & & & 0 & 0 & 0 \\ \cdot & & & & & & & \cdot \\ \cdot & & & & & & & \cdot \\ \cdot & & & & & & & \cdot \\ 0 & \cdot & \cdot & \cdot & & & & 0 \end{bmatrix} 2\alpha C d_f \cos[\omega_0 t + d_f x_0(t)] \tag{5.100}$$

The (1, m + 2)-element is the only nonzero element in the second matrix on the right side.

The received signal is

$$r(t) = z(t) + n(t) = x_{m+1}(t) + n(t) \tag{5.101}$$

where n is a white Gaussian process of spectral height N_0 watts/cps. We see that $\mathbf{h} = x_{m+1}$ and, therefore, that

$$D[\mathbf{h}(t:\mathbf{x})] = \begin{bmatrix} 0 \\ 0 \\ \cdot \\ \cdot \\ \cdot \\ 0 \\ 1 \\ 0 \end{bmatrix} \tag{5.102}$$

The variance equation is coupled to the estimate of **x**, and there is no apparent way to simplify the equation. Because it is quite long but easily derived, we shall not include it here.

The processor equation, Equation 4.1, becomes

$$\dot{\mathbf{x}}^*(t) = \mathbf{f}[t:\mathbf{x}^*(t)] + \frac{1}{N_0} \begin{bmatrix} v^*_{0,m+1}(t) \\ v^*_{1,m+1}(t) \\ \cdot \\ \cdot \\ \cdot \\ v^*_{m+2,m+1}(t) \end{bmatrix} [r(t) - x^*_{m+1}(t)] \tag{5.103}$$

Using Equation 5.99, we then obtain

$$\dot{\mathbf{x}}^*(t) = \mathbf{F}_l \mathbf{x}^*(t) + \begin{bmatrix} 0 \\ 0 \\ \cdot \\ \cdot \\ \cdot \\ 1 \\ 0 \end{bmatrix} 2\alpha C \sin\left[\omega_0 t + d_f x_0^*(t)\right]$$

$$+ \frac{1}{N_0} \begin{bmatrix} v_{0,m+1}^*(t) \\ v_{1,m+1}^*(t) \\ \cdot \\ \cdot \\ \cdot \\ v_{m+2,m+1}^*(t) \end{bmatrix} \left[r(t) - x_{m+1}^*(t)\right] \qquad (5.104)$$

The following two equations are implied by Equation 5.104:

$$\frac{d}{dt} \begin{bmatrix} x_0^*(t) \\ x_1^*(t) \\ \cdot \\ \cdot \\ \cdot \\ x_m^*(t) \end{bmatrix} = \mathbf{F} \begin{bmatrix} x_0^*(t) \\ x_1^*(t) \\ \cdot \\ \cdot \\ \cdot \\ x_m^*(t) \end{bmatrix} + \frac{1}{N_0} \begin{bmatrix} v_{0,m+1}^*(t) \\ v_{1,m+1}^*(t) \\ \cdot \\ \cdot \\ \cdot \\ v_{m,m+1}^*(t) \end{bmatrix} \left[r(t) - x_{m+1}^*(t)\right] \qquad (5.105)$$

and

$$\frac{d}{dt} \begin{bmatrix} x_{m+1}^*(t) \\ x_{m+2}^*(t) \end{bmatrix} = \begin{bmatrix} -2\alpha & 1 \\ -\omega_0^2 & 0 \end{bmatrix} \begin{bmatrix} x_{m+1}^*(t) \\ x_{m+2}^*(t) \end{bmatrix} + \begin{bmatrix} 1 \\ 0 \end{bmatrix} 2\alpha C \sin\left[\omega_0 t + d_f x_0^*(t)\right]$$

$$+ \frac{1}{N_0} \begin{bmatrix} v_{m+1,m+1}^*(t) \\ v_{m+2,m+1}^*(t) \end{bmatrix} \left[r(t) - x_{m+1}^*(t)\right] \qquad (5.106)$$

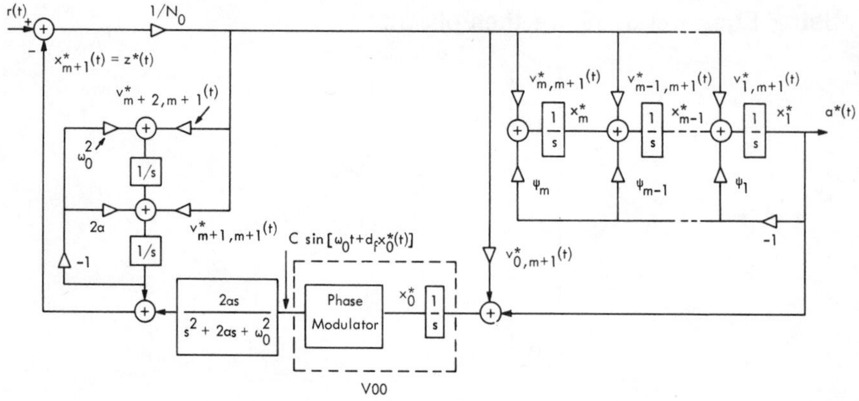

Figure 5.25 Quasi-optimum demodulator for estimating a message transmitted by FM through a fixed channel with memory.

Equations 5.105 and 5.106 lead to the quasi-optimum demodulator shown in Figure 5.25.

Example 5.4.2 Markovian Message, No Modulation, Additive White Noise Channel

In this example, we shall consider the simple model of Figure 5.26a, which cannot be treated by Lehan and Parks' [35] approach to continuous estimation. Attention is restricted to the consideration of a one-dimensional Markovian message x, observed without modulation in white Gaussian noise. The equation describing x is

$$\dot{x}(t) = f[x(t)] + \xi(t) \tag{5.107}$$

where ξ is a white Gaussian process of spectral height X watts/cps. If $f[x(t)] = -k\,x(t)$, then x is Gaussian and the model reduces to the one-dimensional case of Example 5.2.1. Otherwise, x is non-Gaussian and has a stationary amplitude probability density given by

$$p(x) = C \exp\left[\frac{2}{X} \int^{x} f(u)\, du\right] \tag{5.108}$$

where C is a normalization constant and f(x) is assumed to be negative for large positive values of x and positive for large negative values of x. Otherwise f(x) is arbitrary except for the restrictions mentioned in Chapter 2. Equation 5.108 can be derived by use of

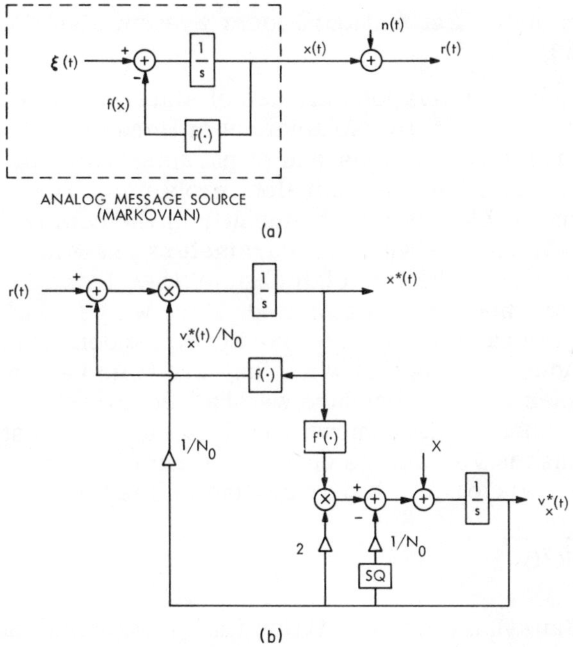

Figure 5.26(a) A model for a one-dimensional Markov process observed in white noise. (b) The quasi-optimum demodulator for estimating a Markov process in white noise.

the Fokker-Planck equation, Equation 2.5. This has been accomplished by Andronov, Pontryagin, and Witt [1] and Barrett [2].

The observed signal is

$$r(t) = x(t) + n(t) \tag{5.109}$$

where n is a white Gaussian process of spectral height N_0 watts/cps. Thus, $\mathbf{h}[t : x(t)] = x(t)$ and $\mathbf{D}[\mathbf{h}(t : x)] = 1$.

The variance and processor equations, Equations 4.1 and 4.2, become

$$\dot{x}^*(t) = f[x^*(t)] + \frac{1}{N_0} v_X^* [r(t) - x^*(t)] \tag{5.110}$$

and

$$\dot{v}_X^*(t) = 2v_X^*(t) \frac{\partial}{\partial x^*} f[x^*(t)] + X - \frac{1}{N_0} v_X^{*2}(t) \tag{5.111}$$

The system for simultaneously generating the quasi-optimum estimate, x^*, and the error variance v_X^* is shown in Figure 5.26b.

Example 5.4.3 Parameter Estimation: Linear System Identification and Process Modeling

We mention only briefly the possible use of state-variable estimation procedures to estimate parameters of linear systems, of parametrized correlation functions, and of parameterized power spectral densities, all of which are equivalent problems. The parameter estimation problem arises frequently in the communication context. One instance is when the parameters associated with the fading processes of the Rayleigh channel (see Example 5.3.4) are unknown and need to be estimated. Here we consider only the case where the parameters are fixed (i.e., random variables), but the technique also applies when they are time variant (i.e., random processes). The procedure we shall describe operates in real time, hence the unknown parameters can be estimated while simultaneously using the channel to communicate.

Let $\mathbf{x}$ be the state vector of a linear system defined by

$$\dot{\mathbf{x}}(t) = \mathbf{F}\mathbf{x}(t) + \mathbf{G}\xi(t) \tag{5.112}$$

where ξ is a white Gaussian noise excitation that may or may not be accessible; ξ may be a known "probe" applied in the laboratory or a fictitious source generating a channel process. Let the observed signal be

$$\mathbf{r}(t) = \mathbf{H}\mathbf{x}(t) + \mathbf{n}(t) \tag{5.113}$$

We assume that $\mathbf{G}$ and $\mathbf{H}$ are known but that $\mathbf{F}$ has unknown entries that are to be estimated along with $\mathbf{x}$. Let $\mathbf{p}$ be the collection of unknown parameters from $\mathbf{F}$. Then, for the simplest case of fixed parameters,

$$\dot{\mathbf{p}} = \mathbf{0} \tag{5.114}$$

It is now apparent that the expanded state vector $\mathbf{z}$,

$$\mathbf{z} = \begin{bmatrix} \mathbf{p} \\ --- \\ \mathbf{x} \end{bmatrix} \tag{5.115}$$

satisfies the differential equation

$$\dot{\mathbf{z}}(t) = \mathbf{f}[\mathbf{z}(t)] + \mathbf{G}_Z\,\xi(t) = \begin{bmatrix} \mathbf{0} \\ ---- \\ \mathbf{F}\mathbf{x}(t) \end{bmatrix} + \begin{bmatrix} \mathbf{0} \\ --- \\ \mathbf{G} \end{bmatrix} \xi(t) \tag{5.116}$$

Because of the products of the components of **z** in **Fx**, clearly **z** is non-Gaussian. Thus, the problem of estimating **p** can be treated using the nonlinear estimation procedures we have described. If the parameters are not fixed, then in place of Equation 5.114, we use their Markovian state vector description.

Very often, of course, there will also be unknown parameters in **G** and these can be appended to **p** in a similar way. In this instance, **z** is still a Markovian state vector, but now the coefficient of the white noise excitation ξ depends on **z**. We have not considered this particular model. However, an estimation procedure to treat it can be developed using exactly the same technique as in Chapter 4.

5.5 SUMMARY AND COMMENTS

In this chapter, we have defined a state-variable model for a wide variety of analog communication systems and channels. Stochastic messages and channel disturbances all appear in the model as components of a single Markovian state vector. The usefulness of the communication model has been illustrated by the application of the state-variable estimation procedure developed in Chapter 4 to the problem of optimum demodulation. Certain of the applications to phase and frequency modulation have also been treated by the alternative maximum *a posteriori* probability or Youla's approach. We note here some of the relative advantages and disadvantages associated with the two approaches.

The following are some advantages of the state-variable approach:

1. The differential equations associated with the approach are easier to solve numerically than the integral equations of the MAP approach.
2. Realizable demodulators result directly.
3. A class of non-Gaussian message and channel disturbances can be treated.

A disadvantage of the state-variable approach is that it is necessary that random processes and linear filtering be representable by equations of state. Thus, Gaussian processes with nonrational spectra cannot be treated exactly—approximations with rational spectra *may* require a large number of states. An example of a particular linear operation that arises and has not yet been adequately treated is that of pure delay.

In Chapter 6, we discuss the analysis of the optimum PM and FM demodulators derived in Examples 5.3.1 and 5.3.2.

6. Analysis of the Performance of Quasi-Optimum PM and FM Demodulators

In this chapter, we shall examine the performance of some of the quasi-optimum PM and FM demodulators derived in the examples of the preceding chapter. The PM case will be presented first. An exact analysis of a quasi-optimum phase estimator for a one-dimensional Gaussian message process is given; the probability density of the estimation error is derived. In the FM case, we first consider the performance for a class of message spectra—the Butterworth class. A comparison is made between actual performance and information-theoretical bounds on the performance. Curves indicating the performance under threshold and bandwidth limitations are given. We then present the results of a computer simulation of a quasi-optimum FM demodulator for estimating a one-dimensional Gaussian message.

The procedure for analyzing quasi-optimum PM and FM demodulators has been given by Van Trees [60] and Viterbi and Cahn [63]. We assume a familiarity with these procedures, particularly those discussed by Van Trees. These authors consider two types of quasi-optimum PM and FM demodulators. The first corresponds to zero-delay estimation of the message; our demodulators fall into this category. The second corresponds to infinite-delay estimation. The modification we require for the infinite-delay case is that of postcascading our demodulators with unrealizable linear filters. These filters can be realized approximately by using delays.

6.1 ANALYSIS OF QUASI-OPTIMUM PM DEMODULATORS

The quasi-optimum PM demodulator is shown in Figure 5.14b. It has the baseband equivalent shown in Figure 6.1. This equivalent has been derived by Van Trees [55, 58, 60] and Viterbi [61]. Here $n'(t)$ is uncorrelated with $a(t)$ and is a white Gaussian process of spectral height $2N_0/C^2$ watts/cps. The estimation error $e_a = a(t) - a^*(t)$ has been minimized by the choice of the loop filter. The minimum-mean-square estimation error σ_a^2 is given

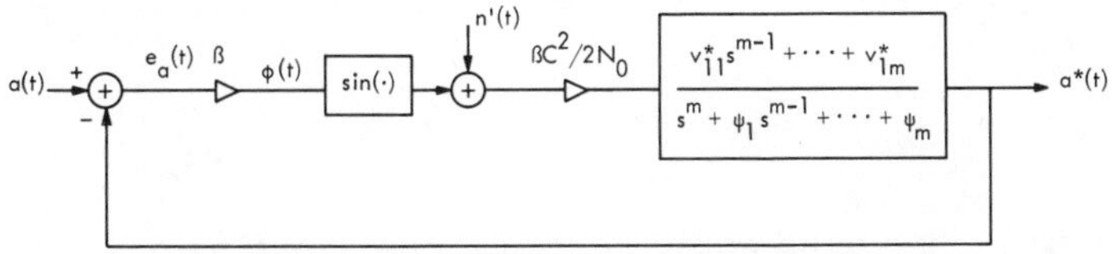

Figure 6.1 Baseband equivalent of the quasi-optimum PM demodulator shown in Figure 5.14b.

by Equation 5.54 provided the conditions under which the demodulator was derived are satisfied. These conditions require that the channel signal-to-noise ratio $C^2/2N_0W_c$ be large; W_c is the channel or receiver-input bandwidth. So long as this condition holds, the total phase error φ is small and, consequently, $\sin \varphi \approx \varphi$ most of the time. As the channel signal-to-noise ratio decreases, the mean-square error increases. Finally, threshold occurs at which point $\sin \varphi$ cannot be approximated by φ and Equation 5.54 no longer describes the performance. Thus, σ_φ^2 is given by

$$\sigma_\varphi^2 = \frac{2N_0}{C^2} \int_{-\infty}^{\infty} \log\left[1 + \frac{\beta^2 C^2}{2N_0} S_a(\omega)\right] \frac{d\omega}{2\pi} \qquad \text{provided } \sigma_\varphi^2 < \sigma_{cr}^2 \tag{6.1}$$

where σ_{cr}^2 is the critical value of σ_φ^2 where threshold occurs; it is roughly 0.25 rad^2.

Equation 6.1 has been used by Viterbi and Cahn [63] to analyze the performance of quasi-optimum zero-delay PM demodulators operating above threshold. The Butterworth class of message spectra was used.

We shall concentrate on the analysis of the optimum demodulation for estimating a Gaussian message that is transmitted by phase modulation. The modulated carrier is received coherently (phase and frequency known initially) in white noise. The message has a first-order Butterworth spectrum. This case was examined in Example 5.3.1.1. The demodulator is shown in Figure 5.15b and its baseband equivalent in Figure 6.2. There $\xi(t)$ and $n'(t)$ are white Gaussian processes of spectral heights 1 and $2N_0/C^2$ watts/cps, respectively. The spectrum of a(t) is $2k/(\omega^2 + k^2)$ watts/cps, and a(t) has a normalized variance of unity.

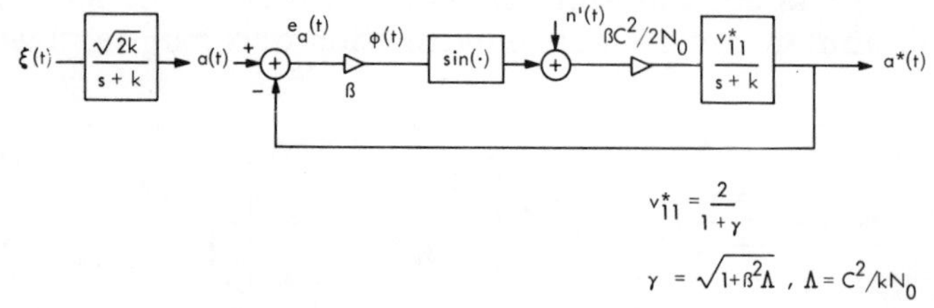

Figure 6.2 Baseband equivalent of a quasi-optimum PM demodulator for a first-order Butterworth message spectrum.

The performance above threshold can be studied by evaluating Equation 6.1 or by using Equation 5.59. The result is, for $\sigma_\varphi^2 < \sigma_{cr}^2$ and $\Lambda = C^2/kN_0$,

$$\sigma_\varphi^2 = \frac{2\beta^2}{1 + \sqrt{1 + \beta^2\Lambda}} \tag{6.2}$$

Equation 6.2 does not provide an accurate description of the performance in the vicinity of threshold and below. This region of operation has been studied by means of computer simulation by Zaorski [72]. We shall present an exact analysis of the performance. The analysis is valid in all regions of operation including threshold and below.

The exact analysis is possible because $\varphi(t)$ is a one-dimensional Markov process for which the associated Fokker-Planck equation can be solved. Use of the Fokker-Planck equation in the study of phase demodulators originated with Tikhonov [52, 53] in the U.S.S.R. His work has been discussed by Viterbi [61]; Tikhonov and Viterbi examined cases where there was no modulation (i.e., $\beta = 0$) and where the loop was not optimum.

Referring to Figure 6.2, we observe that the differential equation describing a*(t) is

$$\dot{a}^*(t) + ka^*(t) = \frac{\beta C^2 v_{11}^*}{2N_1}\,[\sin\varphi + n'(t)] \tag{6.3}$$

where

$$v_{11}^* = \frac{2}{1+\gamma} = \frac{2}{1+\sqrt{1+\beta^2\Lambda}} \qquad \Lambda = C^2/kN_0$$

In terms of the total phase error $\varphi(t)$, we have $a^*(t) = a(t) - (1/\beta)\ \varphi(t)$. We substitute this expression into Equation 6.3 and use

$$\dot{a}(t) + ka(t) = \sqrt{2k}\ \xi(t) \tag{6.4}$$

and we obtain

$$\dot{\varphi}(t) = -k\varphi(t) - \frac{\beta^2 C^2 v_{11}^*}{2N_0} \sin \varphi(t) + \lambda(t) \tag{6.5}$$

where

$$\lambda(t) = \beta\sqrt{2k}\ \xi(t) - \frac{\beta^2 C^2 v_{11}^*}{2N_0}\ n'(t)$$

is a white Gaussian process having a spectral height $(4\beta^2 k\gamma)/(1+\gamma)$ watts/cps where $\gamma = \sqrt{1+\beta^2\ \Lambda}$. As described by Equation 6.5, $\varphi(t)$ is seen to be a one-dimensional Markov process. Consequently, $p(\varphi)$ the steady-state probability density of the total phase error satisfies the Fokker-Planck equation

$$\frac{d}{d\varphi}\left(k\varphi + \frac{k\beta^2\Lambda}{1+\gamma} \sin \varphi\right) p(\varphi) + \frac{2\beta^2 k\gamma}{1+\gamma} \frac{d^2}{d\varphi^2}\, p(\varphi) = 0 \tag{6.6}$$

with the boundary conditions $p\ (\pm\infty) = 0$ and the normalization requirement $\int_{-\infty}^{\infty} p(\varphi)\ d\varphi = 1$. Integrating and using the boundary conditions, we obtain

$$p(\varphi) = K \exp\left(-\frac{1+\gamma}{4\beta^2\gamma}\ \varphi^2 + \frac{\Lambda}{2\gamma} \cos \varphi\right) \tag{6.7}$$

The constant K can be determined by using the normalization requirement and the expansion

$$\exp\left(\frac{\Lambda}{2\gamma} \cos \varphi\right) = \sum_{\nu=-\infty}^{\infty} I_\nu\left(\frac{\Lambda}{2\gamma}\right) \cos \nu\varphi \tag{6.8}$$

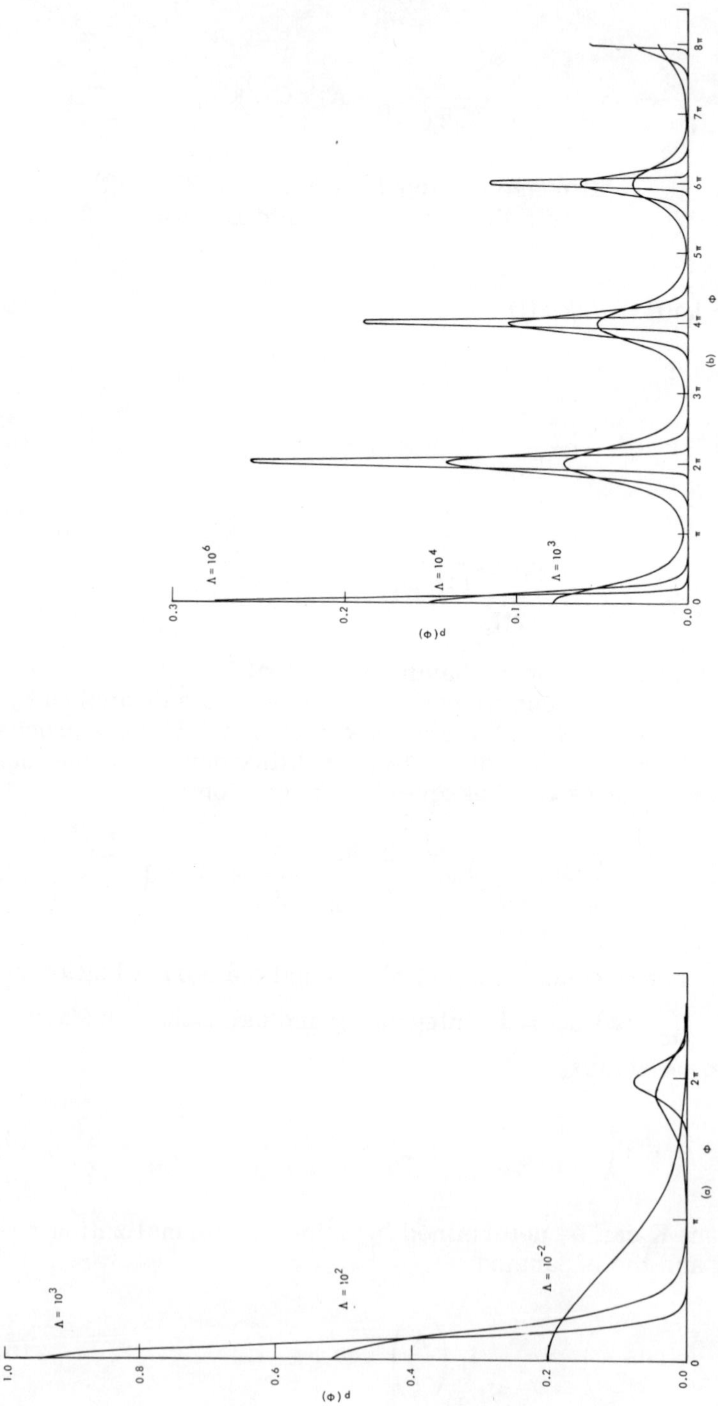

Figure 6.3(a, b) Probability density of the total phase error for an optimum phase demodulator and a first-order Butterworth message spectrum. Λ is the SNR in the message bandwidth.

where $I_\nu(\cdot)$ is a Bessel function of order ν. The final result is

$$p(\varphi) = \frac{\exp\left(-\frac{1+\gamma}{4\beta^2\gamma}\varphi^2 + \frac{\Lambda}{2\gamma}\cos\varphi\right)}{2\beta\sqrt{\frac{\pi\gamma}{1+\gamma}}\sum_{\nu=-\infty}^{\infty} I_\nu\left(\frac{\Lambda}{2\gamma}\right)\exp\left(-\frac{\beta^2\gamma}{1+\gamma}\nu^2\right)} \tag{6.9}$$

Some plots of $p(\varphi)$ for $\varphi \geqslant 0$ and different values of β and $\Lambda = C^2/kN_0$ are given in Figure 6.3. The following observations can be made:

1. Here $p(\varphi)$ is not periodic. Consequently, measurement of φ modulo 2π is not meaningful.
2. The central lobe of $p(\varphi)$ is always larger than the side lobes. This implies that the error has a tendency to return to zero when cycles are skipped.
3. Here $p(\varphi)$ has a Gaussian envelope with variance $2\beta^2\gamma/(1+\gamma)$. Therefore, $p(\varphi)$ has only a central lobe for small index (β small) PM. This implies that no cycle skipping or threshold behavior will be exhibited for small index PM.
4. For large signal-to-noise ratio, the central lobe of $p(\varphi)$ is Gaussian with variance $2\beta^2/(1+\gamma) = v_{11}^*\beta^2$. This is the variance predicted by a linear analysis of the loop.
5. The loop investigated here was originally derived in Example 5.3.1.1 of Chapter 5 as an example of an optimum PM demodulator. Recall we assumed that the received signal was coherent; that is, from Equation 5.56, the signal component of r(t) is $C \sin[\omega_0 t + \beta a(t)]$. However, in practice the received signal is most often incoherent, the signal component being of the form $C \sin[\omega_0 t + \beta a(t) + \omega_\delta t + \theta_\delta]$, where ω_δ and θ_δ are initial frequency and phase offsets. In this case, the loop we have analyzed is, of course, no longer optimum and $p(\varphi)$ is not the density of the loop error. If $\omega_\delta = 0$, but $\theta_\delta \neq 0$, then the average error $E(\varphi/\theta_\delta)$ does not reduce to zero with the first-order loop filter. If $\omega_\delta \neq 0$, the loop fails to achieve lock.

6.2 ANALYSIS OF QUASI-OPTIMUM FM DEMODULATORS

The quasi-optimum FM demodulator is shown in Figure 5.16b. It has the baseband equivalent shown in Figure 6.4. The equivalent is derived in a fashion parallel to that used in the PM case. Here

$\xi(t)$ and $n'(t)$ are uncorrelated white Gaussian processes. The spectral height of $n'(t)$ is $2N_0/C^2$ watts/cps.

Two errors are of interest: (1) $e_a = a(t) - a^*(t)$, the error in the estimation of the message; and (2) $\varphi(t) = d_f e_u(t) = d_f[u(t) - u^*(t)]$, the error in estimating the total phase. The mean-square values of $e_a(t)$ and $\varphi(t)$ are given by Equations 5.66 and 5.65, repectively, provided the conditions under which the demodulator was derived are satisfied. These require that the errors be small. As in the phase-modulation case, threshold occurs when the signal-to-noise ratio decreases and σ_φ^2, the mean-square value of $\varphi(t)$, reaches some critical value σ_{cr}^2, which is roughly 0.25 rad^2. (This value is based on experimental results

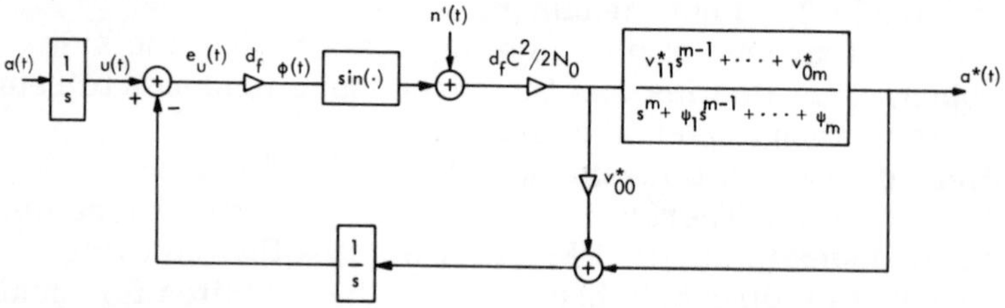

Figure 6.4 Baseband equivalent of the quasi-optimum FM demodulator shown in Figure 5.16b.

presented in Section 6.2.2.1). Equations 5.65 and 5.66 no longer describe the performance below threshold. Rewriting the equations, we have

$$\sigma_\varphi^2 = \frac{2N_0}{C^2} \qquad \text{provided } \sigma_\varphi^2 \leq \sigma_{cr}^2 \tag{6.10}$$

and

$$\sigma_\varphi^2 = \frac{2N_0}{3d_f^2C^2} f^3(0) + F(0) \qquad \text{provided } \sigma_\varphi^2 \leq \sigma_{cr}^2 \tag{6.11}$$

where

$$f(0) = \int_{-\infty}^{\infty} \log \left[1 + \frac{d_f^2\, C^2}{2N_0} \, \frac{S_a(\omega)}{\omega^2} \right] \frac{d\omega}{2\pi}$$

and

$$F(0) = \int_{-\infty}^{\infty} \frac{2N_0}{d_f^2\, C^2}\, \omega^2 \log \left[1 + \frac{d_f^2\, C^2}{2N_0} \, \frac{S_a(\omega)}{\omega^2} \right] \frac{d\omega}{2\pi}$$

Equation 6.11 is the mean-square estimation error for the zero-delay quasi-optimum FM demodulator we have derived. An equation for the mean-square error of the corresponding infinite-delay demodulator has been given by Van Trees [60]. It is

$$\sigma_a^2\bigg|_{\substack{\text{inf.}\\ \text{del.}}} = \int_{-\infty}^{\infty} \frac{S_a(\omega)\,\dfrac{2N_0}{d_f^2 C^2}\,\omega^2}{S_a(\omega) + \dfrac{2N_0}{d_f^2 C^2}\,\omega^2}\,\frac{d\omega}{2\pi} \qquad \sigma_\varphi^2 \leqslant \sigma_{cr}^2 \tag{6.12}$$

6.2.1 Performance of Quasi-Optimum FM Demodulators for a Class of Message Spectra

We have evaluated Equations 6.10 and 6.11 numerically for the Butterworth class of message spectra. For this class,

$$S_a(\omega) = \frac{\dfrac{1}{W_n}}{\left(\dfrac{\omega}{k}\right)^{2n} + 1} \text{ watts/cps} \tag{6.13}$$

where

$$W_n = \frac{k}{2n \sin\left(\dfrac{\pi}{2n}\right)} \text{ cps} \tag{6.14}$$

is the equivalent rectangular bandwidth of the message. Equations 6.10 and 6.11 now become

$$\sigma_{\varphi,n}^2 = \frac{1}{\Lambda}\,\frac{\sin\dfrac{\pi}{2n}}{\dfrac{\pi}{2n}} \int_0^\infty \log\left[1 + \frac{\Lambda\beta^2}{x^2(x^{2n}+1)}\right] dx$$

$$\sigma_{\varphi,n}^2 \leqslant \sigma_{cr}^2 \tag{6.15}$$

and

$$\sigma_{a,n}^2 = \frac{1}{\Lambda\beta^2}\,\frac{\sin\dfrac{\pi}{2n}}{\dfrac{\pi}{2n}}\,\frac{1}{3\pi^2}\left[\int_0^\infty \log\left[1 + \frac{\Lambda\beta^2}{x^2(x^{2n}+1)}\right] dx\right]^3$$

$$+ \frac{1}{\Lambda\beta^2}\,\frac{\sin\dfrac{\pi}{2n}}{\dfrac{\pi}{2n}} \int_0^\infty x^2 \log\left[1 + \frac{\Lambda\beta^2}{x^2(x^{2n}+1)}\right] dx$$

$$\sigma_{\varphi,n}^2 \leqslant \sigma_{cr}^2 \tag{6.16}$$

where $x = \omega/k$, $\Lambda = C^2/2N_0W_n$, and $\beta = d_f/k$. Here Λ is the signal-to-noise ratio in the equivalent rectangular message bandwidth and β is the modulation index. Equation 6.15 can be evaluated for $n = 1$ and $n = \infty$. The results are

$$\sigma^2_{\varphi,1} = \frac{4\beta\Lambda^{-1/2}}{1 + \sqrt{1 + 2\beta\Lambda^{1/2}}} \quad \text{(from Equation 5.71)} \tag{6.17}$$

$$\sigma^2_{\varphi,\infty} = \frac{1}{\Lambda}\left[\log(1 + \Lambda\beta^2) + 2\beta\Lambda^{1/2}\tan^{-1}\frac{1}{\beta\Lambda^{1/2}}\right] \text{[Reference 5]} \tag{6.18}$$

We have plotted $1/\sigma^2_{\varphi,n}$ for $n = 1, 2, 5$, and ∞ in Figures 6.5a to 6.8a. A threshold constraint of $\sigma^2_{cr} = 0.25$ is indicated. The curves accurately describe the performance when $1/\sigma^2_{\varphi,n}$ is above the constraint level.

We have plotted $1/\sigma^2_{a,n}$ for $n = 1, 2, 5$, and ∞ in Figures 6.5b to 6.8b. (The appropriate curve is the one appearing on the extreme right in each figure; the other curves will be explained later.) In the figures, $1/\sigma^2_{a,n}$, for fixed β, is shown only for values of Λ corresponding to above threshold performance. The critical value of Λ for each β is determined from the $1/\sigma^2_{\varphi,n}$ curves; these values are connected to form the threshold constraint line labeled "zero-delay." The following observations can be made:

1. From the $1/\sigma^2_{a,n}$ curves, the slope of the fixed β lines increases from about 0.25 for $n = 1$ to about 0.77 for $n = \infty$. The slope of the fixed β lines determines the rate at which increasing Λ will improve the performance when operating under a fixed bandwidth constraint.
2. From the $1/\sigma^2_{a,n}$ curves, the slope of the threshold constraint line increases from about 1 for $n = 1$ to about 12 for $n = \infty$. The slope of the threshold constraint line determines the rate at which increasing Λ will improve the performance when no bandwidth constraint exists.
3. For any given value of β and Λ, the performance improves as n increases.

For the Butterworth class of message spectra, the equation for the mean-square error in the infinite-delay case, Equation 6.12, becomes

$$\sigma^2_{a,n}\Bigg|_{\substack{\text{inf.}\\ \text{del.}}} = \frac{\sin\frac{\pi}{2n}}{\frac{\pi}{2n}} \int_0^\infty \frac{x^2}{x^{2(n+1)} + x^2 + \Lambda\beta^2}\,dx$$

$$\sigma^2_{\varphi,n} \leq \sigma^2_{cr} \tag{6.19}$$

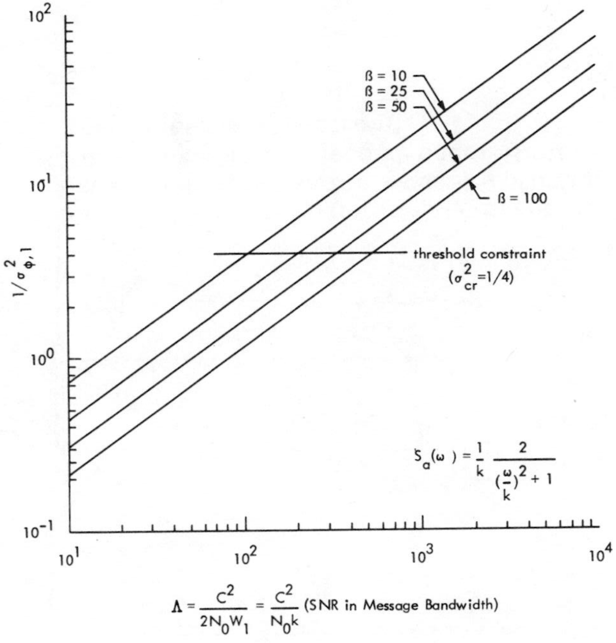

Figure 6.5(a) Inverse mean-square error in estimation of phase for a quasi-optimum FM demodulator. (First-order Butterworth message spectrum.)

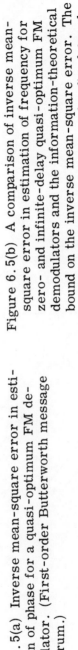

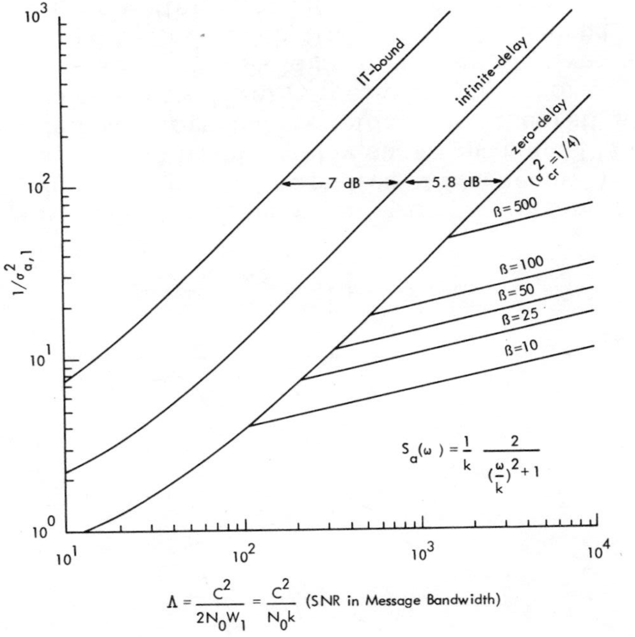

Figure 6.5(b) A comparison of inverse mean-square error in estimation of frequency for zero- and infinite-delay quasi-optimum FM demodulators and the information-theoretical bound on the inverse mean-square error. The above threshold performance for fixed β and zero delay is also indicated. (First-order Butterworth message spectrum.)

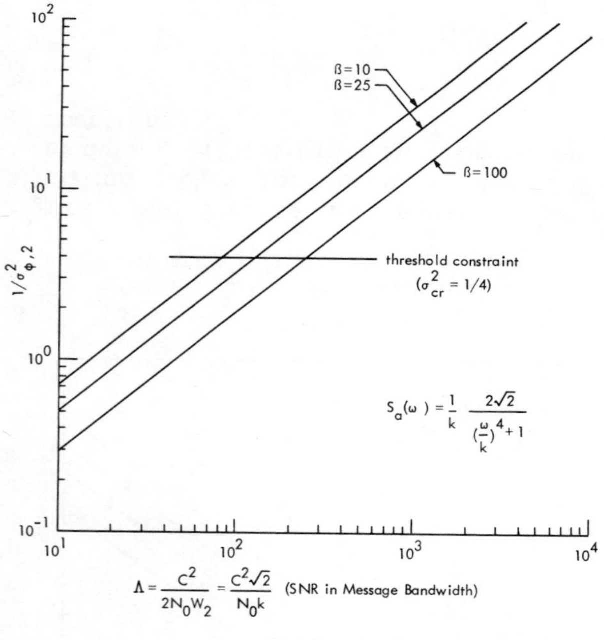

Figure 6.6(a) Inverse mean-square error in estimation of phase for a quasi-optimum FM demodulator. (Second-order Butterworth message spectrum).

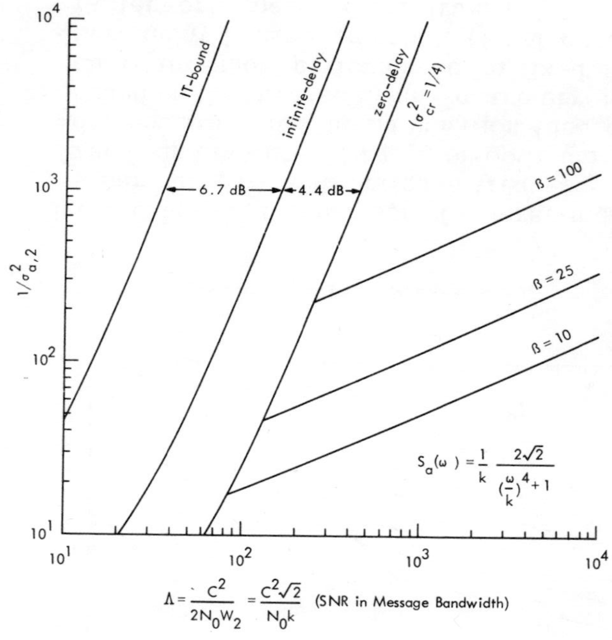

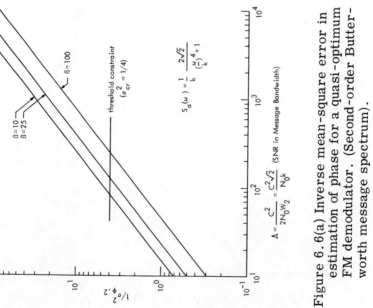

Figure 6.6(b) A comparison of inverse mean-square error in estimation of frequency for zero- and infinite-delay quasi-optimum FM demodulators and the information theoretical bound on the inverse mean-square error. The above threshold performance for fixed β and zero delay is also indicated. (Second order Butterworth message spectrum.)

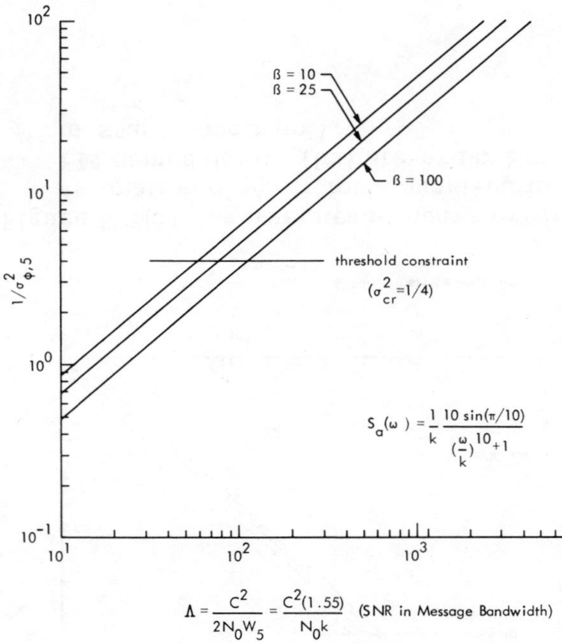

Figure 6.7(a) Inverse mean-square error in estimation of phase for a quasi-optimum FM demodulator. (Fifth-order Butterworth message spectrum.)

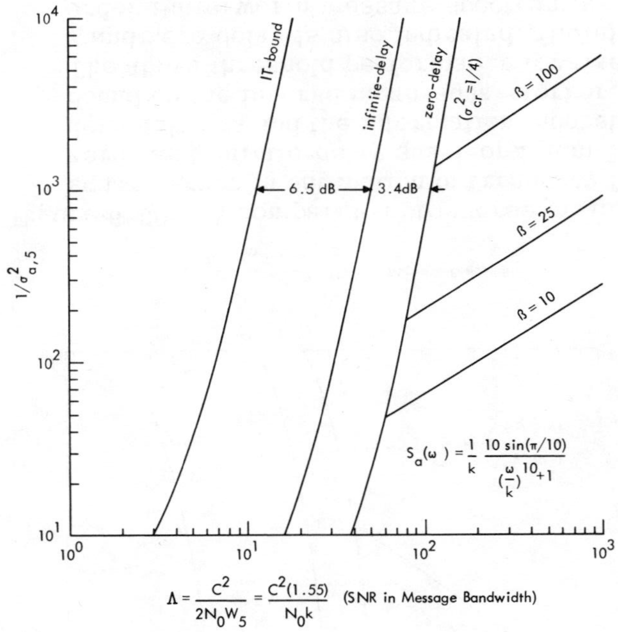

Figure 6.7(b) A comparison of inverse mean-square error in estimation of frequency for zero- and infinite-delay quasi-optimum FM demodulators and the information theoretical bound on the inverse mean-square error. The above threshold performance for fixed β and zero delay is also indicated. (Fifth-order Butterworth message spectrum.)

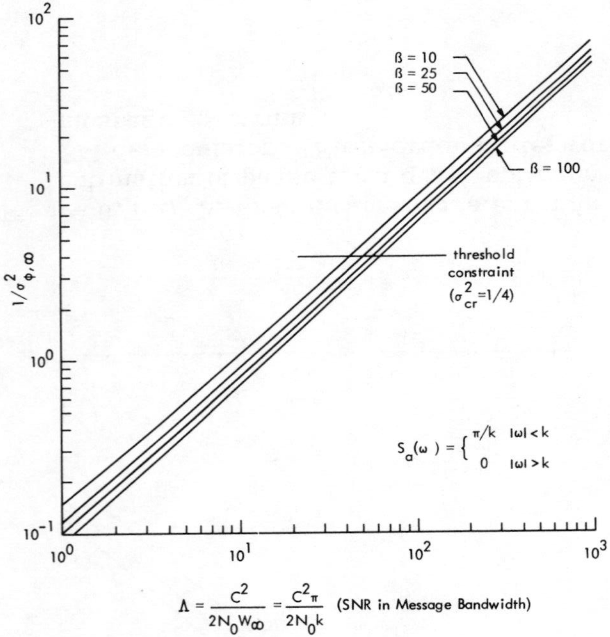

Figure 6.8(a) Inverse mean-square error in estimation of phase for a quasi-optimum FM demodulator. (Infinite-order Butterworth message spectrum.)

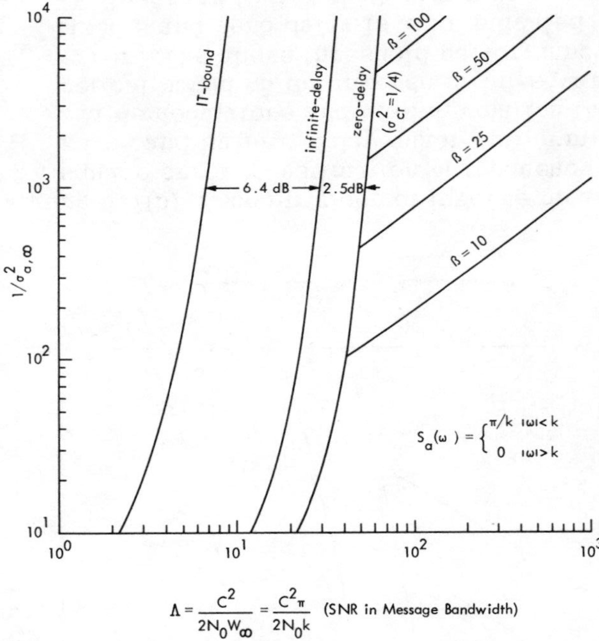

Figure 6.8(b) A comparison of inverse mean-square error in estimation of frequency for zero- and infinite-delay quasi-optimum FM demodulators and the information theoretical bound on the inverse mean-square error. The above threshold performance for fixed β and zero delay is also indicated. (Infinite order Butterworth message spectrum.)

where x, Λ, and β are as defined previously. Equation 6.19 can be evaluated for n = 1 and n = ∞. The results are

$$\sigma^2_{\hat{a},n}\Big|_{\substack{\text{inf.}\\ \text{del.}}} = \frac{1}{\sqrt{1 + 2\beta\Lambda^{1/2}}} \qquad \sigma^2_{\hat{\varphi},1} \leq \sigma^2_{\hat{c}r} \tag{6.20}$$

and

$$\sigma^2_{\hat{a},\infty}\Big|_{\substack{\text{inf.}\\ \text{del.}}} = 1 - \beta\Lambda^{1/2} \tan^{-1} \frac{1}{\beta\Lambda^{1/2}} \qquad \sigma^2_{\hat{\varphi},\infty} \leq \sigma^2_{\hat{c}r} \tag{6.21}$$

We have plotted $1/\sigma^2_{\hat{a},n}$ for n = 1, 2, 5, and ∞ for the infinite-delay case in Figures 6.5b to 6.8b. For clarity, only the threshold performance line, labeled "infinite-delay," is shown. The amount of threshold improvement that can be attained by adding delay is evident; it ranges from 6 dB for n = 1 to 2.5 dB for n = ∞.

Goblick [21] has presented information-theoretical bounds on the performance attainable with any modulation-demodulation scheme used for communicating Gaussian messages whose spectra are of the Butterworth class. Van Trees [57] has discussed the use of these bounds for evaluating the performance of angle-modulation schemes. We have included the bounds in Figures 6.5b to 6.8b. It is seen that the actual performance of a zero-delay, quasi-optimum FM demodulator ranges from about 13 dB, for n = 1, to about 9 dB, for n = ∞, away from the theoretical bound. These values are based on the particular threshold constraint level of 0.25 rad^2 that we have chosen to match experimental results mentioned in Section 6.2.2.1. The values increase as the constraint level is made smaller.

6.2.2 Performance of a Quasi-Optimum FM Demodulator for a First-Order Butterworth Message Spectrum: Simulation Results

In this section, we shall present the results of a computer simulation of the FM demodulator derived in Example 5.3.2.1 and shown in Figure 5.17b. The baseband equivalent for the demodulator is shown in Figure 6.9. Here $\xi(t)$ and $n'(t)$ are uncor-

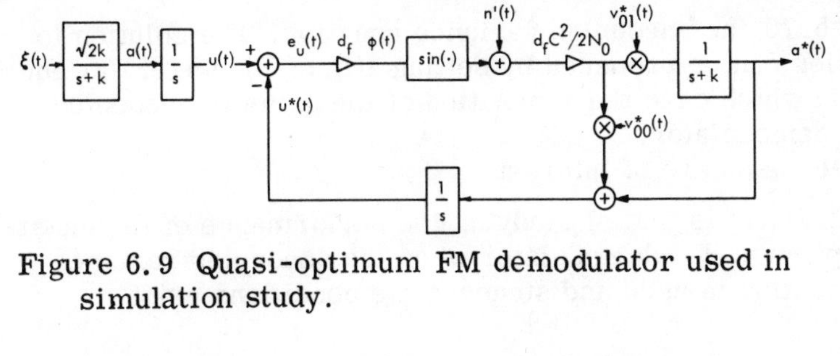

Figure 6.9 Quasi-optimum FM demodulator used in simulation study.

related white Gaussian processes with spectral heights of unity and $2N_0/C^2$ watts/cps, respectively. As mentioned in the discussion of the example (see Section 5.3.2.1), the two time-varying gains $v^*_{00}(t)$ and $v^*_{01}(t)$ were generated in two ways. The first way was by simulating Equation 5.69, the coupled variance equation. The equation is shown in block diagram form in Figure 6.10a; the baseband equivalent is shown in Figure 6.10b. Here $n''(t)$ is a white Gaussian process that is uncorrelated with $\xi(t)$ and $n'(t)$; it has a spectral height of $2N_0/C^2$ watts/cps. The baseband equivalent of the variance equation is coupled to that of the demodulator by $\varphi(t)$, the error in estimating the total phase $d_f u(t)$. The second way of generating the two time-varying gains was by simulating

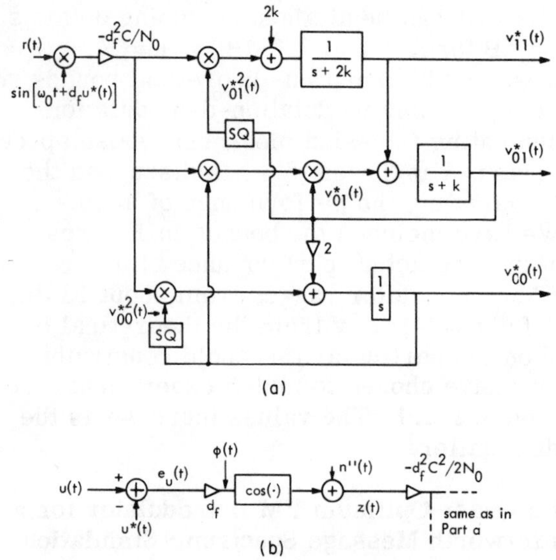

Figure 6.10 (a) Processor for generating solution to the coupled variance equation. (b) Its baseband equivalent.

Equation 5.70, the uncoupled variance equation. The solution to the equation can be produced by setting $z(t)$, of Figure 6.10b, equal to unity, in which case the generation of the gains is uncoupled from the demodulator.

Three cases are of interest:

1. The first is that of studying the performance of the quasi-optimum FM demodulator when the uncoupled variance equation is used and steady-state conditions exist.

2. The second is that of studying the performance when the uncoupled variance equation is used and transient conditions exist. In this instance, the variance equation can be simulated either simultaneously with the demodulator or in advance.
3. The third is that of studying the performance when the coupled variance equation is used and transient conditions exist. The variance equation must be simulated simultaneously with the demodulator.

6.2.2.1 *Performance of the uncoupled variance Equation: steady state.* In this case, the gains $v_{00}^*(t)$ and $v_{01}^*(t)$ of Figure 6.9 are constants that are given explicitly by Equations 5.71 and 5.72. Zaorski [72] has simulated the demodulator for this steady-state case, and we have reproduced his results in Figures 6.11a and 6.11b. The theoretical performance curves of Figures 6.5a and 6.5b are superimposed on his results. These are seen to match the actual performance curves very well above threshold.

It can be demonstrated that the error in estimating the message $e_a(t) = a(t) - a^*(t)$ and the error in estimating the total phase $\varphi(t) = d_f[u(t) - u^*(t)]$ form a two-dimensional Markov process. For this purpose, differential equations describing the two errors can be derived following the procedure used to derive Equation 6.5. We obtain

$$\dot{e}_a(t) = -ke_a(t) - \frac{v_{01}^* d_f C^2}{2N_0} \sin \varphi(t) + \left[\sqrt{2k}\, \xi(t) - \frac{v_{01}^* d_f C^2}{2N_0} n'(t) \right] \tag{6.22}$$

$$\dot{\varphi}(t) = d_f e_a(t) - \frac{v_{00}^* d_f^2 C^2}{2N_0} \sin \varphi(t) - \left[\frac{v_{00}^* d_f^2 C^2}{2N_0} n'(t) \right] \tag{6.23}$$

The bracketed expression in each equation is a white Gaussian process. The two-dimensional vector with $e_a(t)$ and $\varphi(t)$ as its components satisfies an equation of the form of Equation 2.1 and is therefore a two-dimensional Markov process. Unfortunately, the corresponding Fokker-Planck equation for the joint probability density $p(e_a, \varphi)$ appears to be analytically intractable. However, it is possible to obtain an approximate expression for $p(\varphi)$, the steady-state probability density for the phase error, by using approximation procedures introduced by Viterbi [61]. The steady-

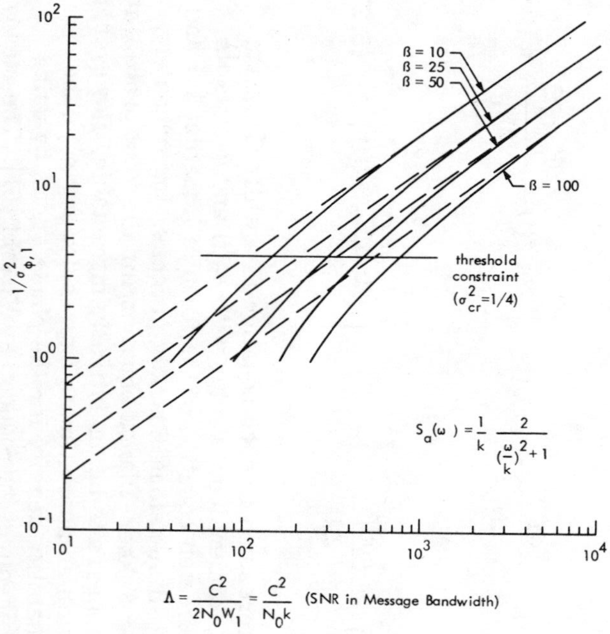

Figure 6.11(a) Solid Lines: Experimental performance of a quasi-optimum FM demodulator in steady state (from Zaorski [72]). Dashed Lines: Theoretical performance (from Figure 6.5a).

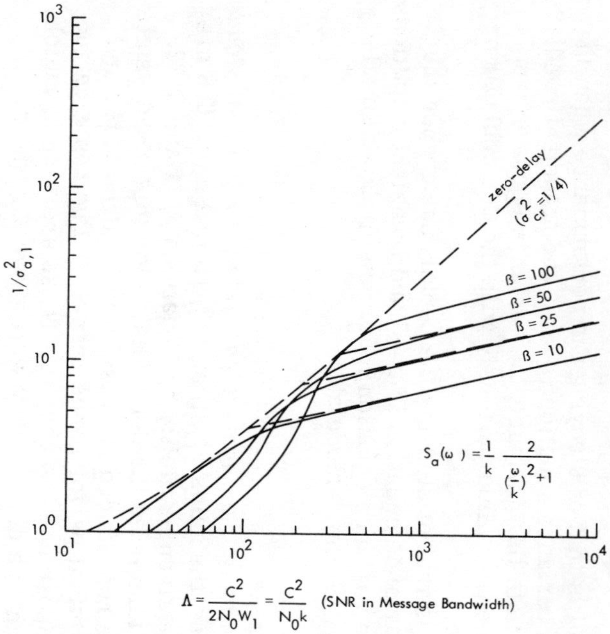

Figure 6.11(b) Solid Lines: Experimental performance of a Quasi-optimum FM demodulator in steady state (from Zaorski [72]). Dashed Lines: Theoretical performance (from Figure 6.5b).

state Fokker-Planck equation for $p(e_a, \varphi)$ is

$$\frac{\partial}{\partial e_a}\left[ke_a + \frac{v_{01}^* d_f C^2}{2N_0}\sin\varphi\right]p(e_a,\varphi)$$

$$+\frac{\partial}{\partial\varphi}\left[-d_f e_a + \frac{v_{00}^* d_f^2 C^2}{2N_0}\sin\varphi\right]p(e_a,\varphi)$$

$$+\left[k + \frac{v_{01}^{*2} d_f^2 C^2}{2N_0}\right]\frac{\partial^2}{\partial e_a^2}\;p(e_a,\varphi)$$

$$+\left[\frac{v_{00}^{*2} d_f^4 C^2}{2N_0}\right]\frac{\partial^2}{\partial\varphi^2}\;p(e_a,\varphi)$$

$$+\left[\frac{v_{00}^* v_{01}^* d_f^3 C^2}{2N_0}\right]\frac{\partial^2}{\partial e_a\,\partial\varphi}\;p(e_a,\varphi) = 0 \qquad (6.24)$$

Integration of Equation 6.24 with respect to e_a results in the following differential equation for $p(\varphi)$:

$$\frac{d}{d\varphi}\left[-d_f E(e_a \mid \varphi) + \frac{v_{00}^* d_f^2 C^2}{2N_0}\sin\varphi\right]p(\varphi)$$

$$+\left[\frac{v_{00}^{*2} d_f^4 C^2}{2N_0}\right]\frac{d^2}{d\varphi^2}\;p(\varphi) = 0 \qquad (6.25)$$

where $E(e_a \mid \varphi)$ is the conditional expectation of e_a with φ given and where appropriate boundary conditions have been assumed. Dividing Equation 6.25 by k and using $\beta = d_f/k$ and Equation 5.71, we obtain

$$\frac{d}{d\varphi}\left[\frac{d}{d\varphi}\,p(\varphi) + \frac{\Lambda^{1/2}\gamma}{2\beta}\sin\varphi\; p(\varphi) - \frac{\gamma^2}{4\beta}\,E(e_a \mid \varphi)p(\varphi)\right] = 0 \qquad (6.26)$$

where $\gamma = 1 + \sqrt{1 + 2\beta\Lambda^{1/2}}$ and $\Lambda = C^2/kN_0$ is the signal-to-noise ratio in the message bandwidth.

It does not appear possible to evaluate exactly the conditional expectation $E(e_a \mid \varphi)$ without solving the two-dimensional Fokker-Planck equation, Equation 6.24, for $p(e_a, \varphi)$. However, using the same argument as Viterbi, we can determine its approximate form. Integrating Equation 6.22 and taking conditional expectation, we have

$$E[e_a(t) \mid \varphi(t)] = -\frac{v_{01}^* d_f C^2}{2N_0} \int_0^\infty e^{-k\mu}\, E\,[\sin \varphi(t-\mu) \mid \varphi(t)]\, d\mu \tag{6.27}$$

If the signal-to-noise ratio Λ is large, the phase error $\varphi(t)$ is presumably small most of the time. Consequently, $\sin \varphi(t-\mu) = \varphi(t-\mu)$, approximately, most of the time and

$$E\,[\sin \varphi(t-\mu) \mid \varphi(t)] \doteq \rho_\varphi(\mu)\, \varphi(t) \doteq \rho_\varphi(\mu) \sin \varphi(t) \tag{6.28}$$

because $\varphi(t-\mu)$ and $\varphi(t)$ are approximately jointly normal; here $\rho_\varphi(\mu)$ is the normalized correlation coefficient of $\varphi(t)$ in the linear approximation. When Equation 6.28 is substituted into Equation 6.27, it is seen that the conditional expectation $E[e_a(t) \mid \varphi(t)]$ is approximately proportional to $\sin \varphi(t)$ when Λ is large; the proportionality constant, of course, depends on the explicit form of $\rho_\varphi(\mu)$. Using these observations, Equation 6.28 becomes for large Λ

$$\frac{d}{d\varphi}\left[\frac{d}{d\varphi}\, p(\varphi) + a \sin \varphi\; p(\varphi)\right] = 0 \tag{6.29}$$

where a is some constant to be determined.

The solution to Equation 6.29 that is normalized modulo 2π is

$$p(\varphi) = \frac{e^{a \cos \varphi}}{2\pi\, I_0(a)} \qquad |\varphi| \leqslant \pi \tag{6.30}$$

where I_0 is a zero-order Bessel function. To evaluate the constant a, which increases with Λ, we use the asymptotic approximation

$$I_0(a) \doteq \frac{e^a}{\sqrt{2\pi a}} \qquad a \gg 1$$

to obtain for large a

$$p(\varphi) \doteq \frac{e^{a(\cos \varphi - 1)}}{\sqrt{\dfrac{2\pi}{a}}}$$

$$= \frac{1}{\sqrt{\dfrac{2\pi}{a}}} \exp\left(-\frac{a\varphi^2}{2} + \frac{a\varphi^4}{4!} - \cdots\right)$$

For φ small, $p(\varphi)$ is nearly normal with variance parameter 1/a. This variance must be the same as that resulting from the linear analysis of the demodulator, Equation 5.71; for example,

$$\frac{1}{a} = d_f^2 v_{00}^* = \frac{4\beta\Lambda^{-1/2}}{1 + \sqrt{1 + 2\beta\Lambda^{1/2}}} \tag{6.31}$$

Thus, within the approximation, $p(\varphi)$ is given by Equation 6.30 where a is specified by Equation 6.31.

To test the accuracy of this approximate analysis, Koontz [28] numerically evaluated the integral

$$\int_{-\pi}^{\pi} \varphi^2\, p(\varphi)\, d\varphi \tag{6.32}$$

where $p(\varphi)$ is given by Equation 6.30 and compared the result to the simulation results of Zaorski. The comparison is indicated in Figure 6.12. Shown in Figure 6.12 are: (1), the approximate non-

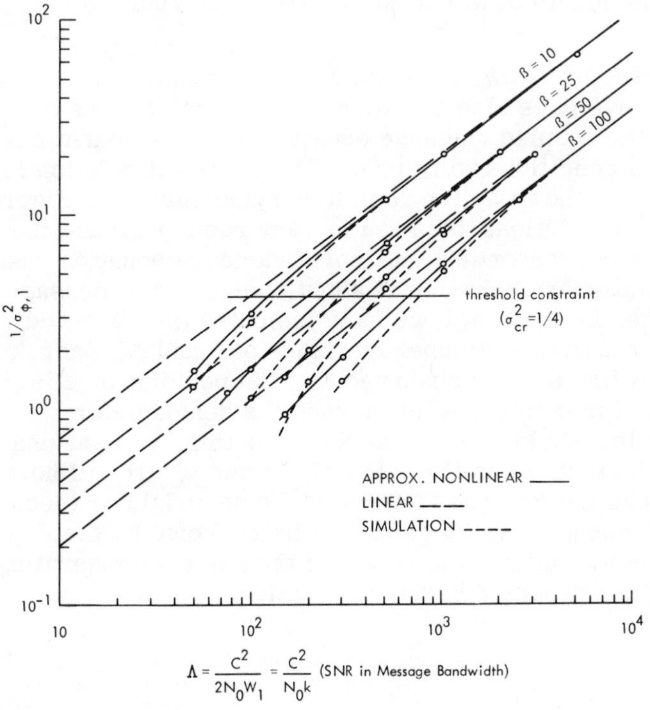

Figure 6.12 Comparison of approximate theoretical performance to experimental performance. (First-order Butterworth message spectrum.)

linear result obtained by numerically integrating Equation 6.32; (2), the simulation results of Zaorski; and (3), the approximate linear results reproduced from Figure 6.5a. The nonlinear approximations are seen to lead to a substantially better estimate of performance than the linear approximations, especially in the vicinity and above the threshold constraint level.

6.2.2.2 *Performance with the uncoupled variance equation: transient case.* We have simultaneously simulated the demodulator and the uncoupled variance equation in the transient case. We assumed that at the initial observation time $t_0 = 0$, the message was known to be zero, $a(0) = 0$. The appropriate initial condition for the variance equation is then $\mathbf{V}^*(0) = \mathbf{0}$. The transient solution for two components of the uncoupled variance equation $v^*_{00}(t)$ and $v^*_{11}(t)$ are shown in Figures 6.13 to 6.16† as the smooth curves. It is seen that the steady-state solution is reached in about one-fourth the message correlation time. This accounts for the fact that the long-term (~150 message correlation times) performance we observed was identical to that observed by Zaorski.

6.2.2.3 *Performance with the coupled variance equation: transient case.* We have also simultaneously simulated the demodulator and the coupled variance equation in the transient case. The same initial conditions were used. The transient solution for $v^*_{00}(t)$ and $v^*_{11}(t)$ is shown as the rapidly varying curves in Figures 6.13 to 6.16. The solutions are seen to vary rapidly around the solutions for the corresponding uncoupled variance equation case. They reach a stationary behavior in about one-fourth a message correlation time. In Table 6.1, we have indicated the observed performance for a limited number of values of β and Λ. Zaorski's results are also listed. It is observed that the performance is nearly the same for both cases, even when the demodulator operates below threshold. We can account for this by observing that the rapid fluctuations in the gains $v^*_{00}(t)$ and $v^*_{01}(t)$ will not propagate through the low-pass filters of the demodulator (see Figure 6.9). Consequently, the gains can be replaced by their short-term time averages. The result is the same as generating the gains with the uncoupled variance equation.

---

† The small discontinuities in the curves are due to truncation errors in the numerical simulation.

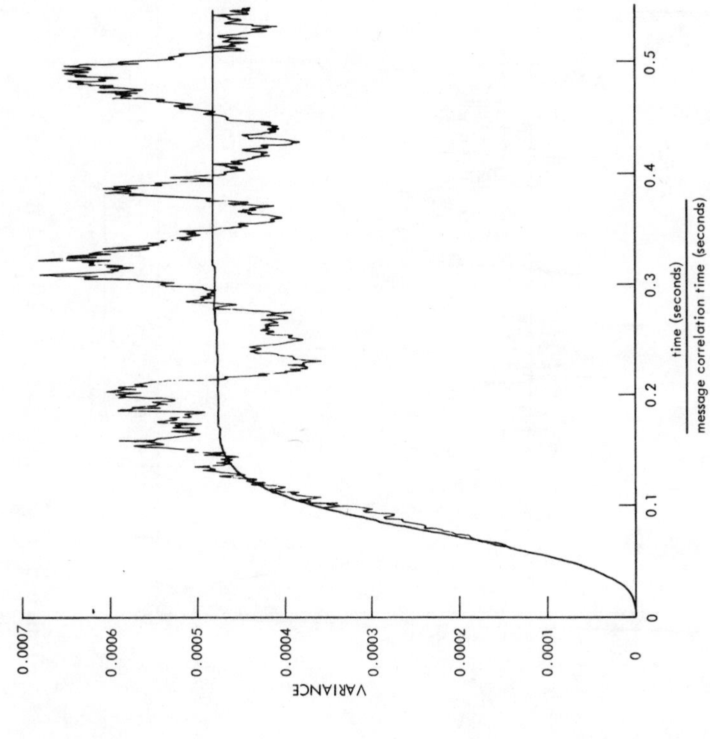

Figure 6.13 $v^*_{00}(t)$ for $\beta = 10$ and $\Lambda = 1000$.

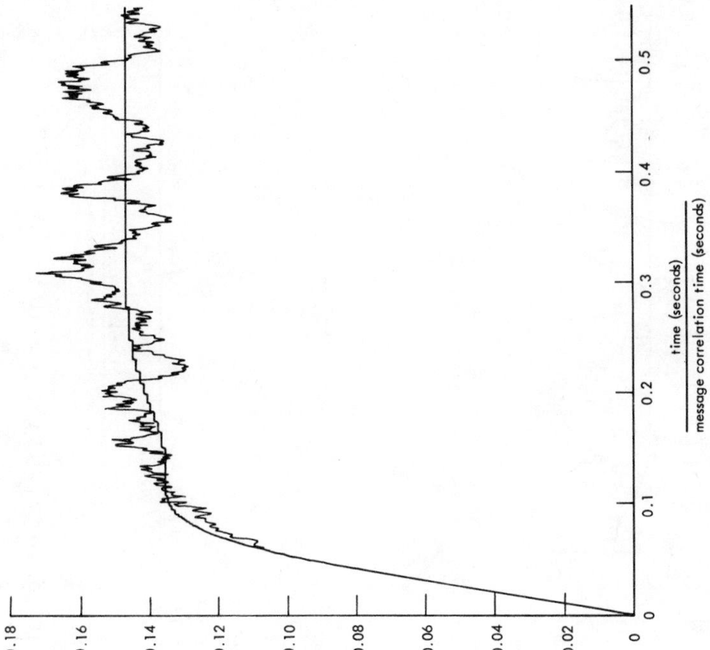

Figure 6.14 $v^*_{11}(t)$ for $\beta = 10$ and $\Lambda = 1000$.

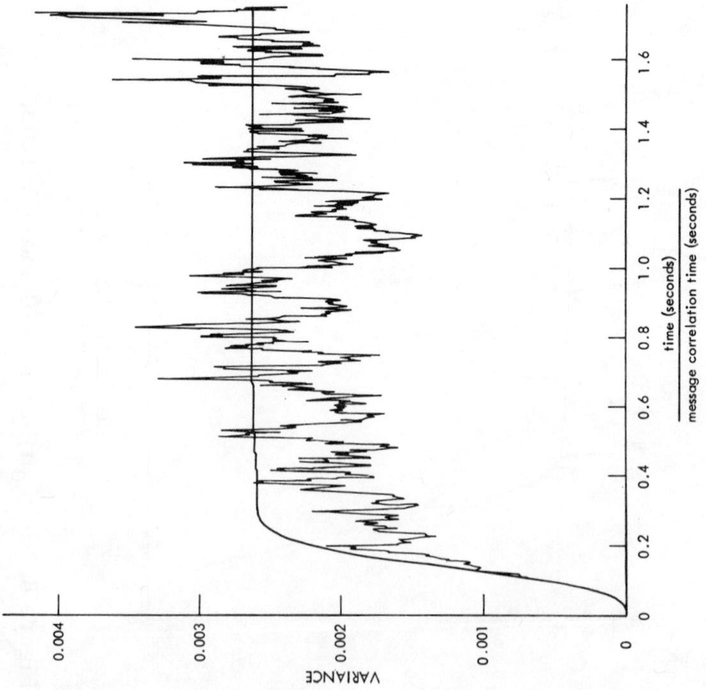

Figure 6.15 $v^*_{00}(t)$ for $\beta = 10$ and $\Lambda = 100$.

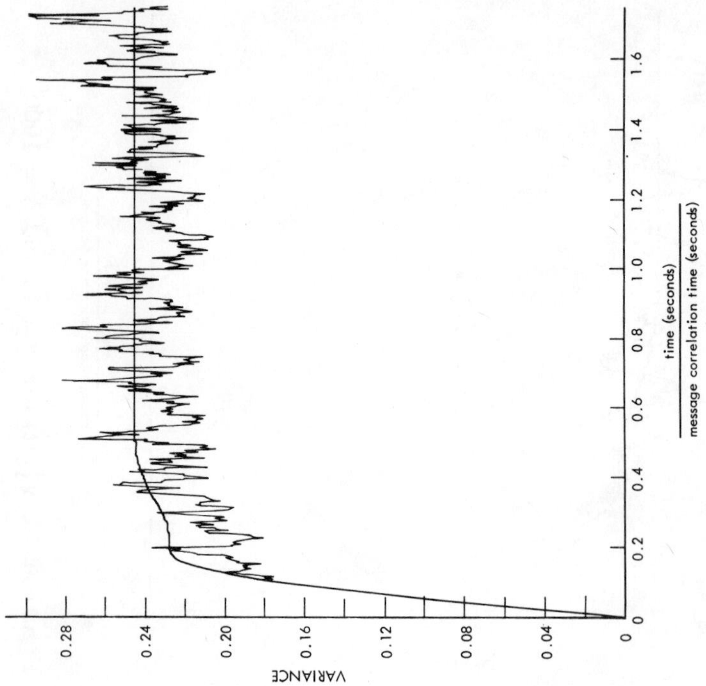

Figure 6.16 $v^*_{11}(t)$ for $\beta = 10$ and $\Lambda = 100$.

Table 6.1. A Comparison of Simulation Results Using the Coupled and Uncoupled Variance Equation.

β	$\Lambda = C^2/N_0k$	Length of Simulation (Message Correlation Times)	Coupled Variance Equation		Uncoupled Variance Equation	
			$1/\sigma^2_{\varphi,1}$	$1/\sigma^2_{\varphi,1}$	$1/\sigma^2_{\varphi,1}$	$1/\sigma^2_{\varphi}$
10	1000	170	20.4	6.7	20.0	6.8
10	100	183	2.9	3.5	2.8	3.8
10	40	46	0.9	2.8		
50	1000	9	8.2	13.5	7.8	13.8

6.3 SUMMARY AND COMMENTS

In this final chapter, we have analyzed the performance of the quasi-optimum demodulators derived in Chapter 5 for estimating, (1) a first-order Gauss-Markov process transmitted coherently by phase modulation (Section 6.1); and (2) a class of Gauss-Markov processes transmitted coherently by frequency modulation (Section 6.2.1). We have indicated (Figures 6.5b to 6.8b) the degree to which the performance of our quasi-optimum FM demodulators approaches the best attainable performance using any form of modulation and demodulation. Finally, by means of simulations, we have investigated (Section 6.2.2) the accuracy of our performance analysis of a demodulator for estimating a first-order Gauss-Markov process transmitted coherently by frequency modulation. In the simulations, we also investigated (Section 6.2.2.3) the validity of the approximations made to the variance equation in Example 5.3.1 of Chapter 5. The approximations appear to be valid.

Notation

$\mathbf{v}(t)$	Lowercase boldface letters denote column vectors.
$v_i(t)$	The i-th component of $\mathbf{v}(t)$.
$\frac{d}{dt}\mathbf{v}(t)$	A vector whose i-th component is $(d/dt)\, v_i(t)$.
$\mathbf{M}(t)$	Uppercase boldface letters denote matrices.
$\mathbf{M}'(t)$	Transpose of $\mathbf{M}(t)$.
$\mathbf{M}^{-1}(t)$	Inverse of $\mathbf{M}(t)$.
$[\mathbf{M}(t)]_{ij}$	The (i, j)-element of M(t).
$\mathbf{f}[t:\mathbf{v}(t)]$	A column vector whose components are nonlinear no-memory time-varying transformations of $\mathbf{v}(t)$.
$\mathbf{D}[\mathbf{f}(t:\mathbf{v})]$	The Jacobian matrix associated with $\mathbf{f}[t:\mathbf{v}(t)]$. The (i-row, j-column)-element of $\mathbf{D}[\mathbf{f}(t:\mathbf{v})]$ is $\partial/\partial v_i\, f_j\, [t:v(t)]$.
$\hat{\mathbf{v}}(t)$	Circumflex denotes the exact minimum-mean-square error estimate.
$\mathbf{v}^*(t)$	Asterisk denotes the approximate minimum-mean-square error estimate.
$\mathbf{v}_{t_0,t}$	Denotes the set of waveforms $\{\mathbf{v}(\tau) : t_0 \leq \tau \leq t\}$.

References

1. A. Andronov, L. Pontryagin, and A. Witt, "On the Statistical Investigation of Dynamical Systems," *J. Expr. Theor. Phys.*, **3**, 3, 165, 1933.
2. J. F. Barrett, "Application of Kolmogorov's Equations to Randomly Distributed Automatic Control Systems," Auto. and Remote Cont., *Proc. of First IFAC Congress*, Moscow, **2**, 724-733, 1960.
3. R. W. Bass, V. D. Norum, and L. Schwartz, "Optimal Multichannel Nonlinear Filtering," Rept. SSD-50064R, Hughes Aircraft Co., Space Systems Div., Los Angeles, Calif., Aug. 1965.
4. R. H. Battin, "A Statistical Optimizing Navigation Procedure for Space Flight," *Amer. Roc. Soc. J.*, 1681-1696, Sept. 1962.
5. H. Becker, T. Chang, and J. Lawton, "Investigation of Advanced Analog Communications Techniques," TR RADC-TR-65-81, Rome Air Development Center, Res. and Dev. Div., Griffiss Air Force Base, N.Y., Mar. 1965. (Also available as AD 613703 from DDC.)
6. A. T. Bharucha-Reid, *Elements of the Theory of Markov Processes and their Applications*, McGraw-Hill Book Co., New York, 1960.
7. I. A. Bol'shakov and V. G. Repin, "Problems of Nonlinear Filtration: I. The Case of One Parameter," *Automation and Remote Control*, **22**, 4, 397-408, Apr. 1961.
8. I. A. Bol'shakov and V. G. Repin, "Questions of Nonlinear Filtering: II. Multidimensional Case," *Automation and Remote Control*, **25**, 12, 1499-1511, May 1965.
9. R. S. Bucy, "Nonlinear Filtering Theory," *IEEE Trans. Auto. Cont.* (Correspondence), **AC-10**, No. 2, 198, Apr. 1965.
10. H. Cox, "Estimation of State-Variables and Parameters for Noisy Dynamic Systems," Sc.D. Thesis, Department of Electrical Engineering, M.I.T., Cambridge, Mass., 1963.
11. H. Cox, "On the Estimation of State Variables and Parameters for Noisy Dynamic Systems," *IEEE Trans. Auto. Cont.*, **AC-9**, No. 1, Jan. 1964.
12. W. Davenport and W. Root, *An Introduction to the Theory of Random Signals and Noise*, McGraw-Hill Book Co., New York, 1958.
13. P. DeRusso, R. Roy, and C. Close, *State Variables for Engineers*, John Wiley & Sons, Inc., New York, 1965.
14. D. M. Detchmendy and R. Srider, "Sequential Estimation of States and Parameters in Noisy Nonlinear Dynamic Systems," *Trans. ASME*, 362-368, June 1966.
15. J. A. Develet, "A Threshold Criterion for Phase-Lock Demodulation," *Proc. IEEE*, **51**, 2, 349-356, Feb. 1963.

16. J. L. Doob, *Stochastic Processes*, John Wiley & Sons, Inc., New York, 1953.
17. E. B. Dynkin, *Markov Processes*, **1** and **2**, Academic Press, New York, 1965.
18. W. A. Edson, "Noise in Oscillators," *Proc. IRE*, **48**, 1454-1466, Aug. 1960.
19. A. E. Fein, R. Heller, and C. Helstrom, "Analog Coding," Westinghouse Electric Corp., Baltimore, Md., 1965. (Also available from DDC as AD 626388.)
20. J. R. Fisher, "Optimal Nonlinear Filtering," *Rept. 66-5*, Dept. of Engrg., University of California at Los Angeles, Jan. 1966.
21. T. Goblick, "Theoretical Limitations on the Transmission of Data from Analog Sources," *IEEE Trans. Info. Th.*, **IT-11**, **4**, 558-567, Oct. 1965.
22. Y. C. Ho and R. C. K. Lee, "A Bayesian Approach to Problems in Stochastic Estimation and Control," *IEEE Trans. Auto. Control*, 333-339, Oct. 1964.
23. K. Ito, "On Stochastic Differential Equations," *Mem. Am. Math. Soc.*, **4**, 1-51, 1951.
24. A. H. Jazwinski, "Filtering for Nonlinear Dynamical Systems," *IEEE Trans. Auto. Contr.* (Correspondence). 765-766, Oct. 1966.
25. R. E. Kalman, "New Methods and Results in Linear Prediction and Filtering Theory," *RIAS Tech. Rpt. 61-1*, Baltimore, Md., 1961.
26. R. E. Kalman and R. Bucy, "New Results in Linear Filtering and Prediction Theory," *ASME J. Basic Eng.*, **83**, 95-108, Mar. 1961.
27. A. Kolmogorov, "Interpolation und Extrapolation von stationären zufälligen Folgen," *Bulletin de l'académie des sciences de U.R.S.S., Ser. Math.*, **5**, 3-14, 1941.
28. W. L. G. Koontz, "Numerical Analysis of a Quasi-Optimum FM Demodulator," S.M. Thesis, Department of Electrical Engineering, M.I.T., Cambridge, Mass., Sept. 1967.
29. N. K. Kul'man, "Optimum Reception of a Signal of Variable Frequency and Amplitude in the Presence of Noise," *Radio Eng. and Elec. Physics*, **9**, No. 5, 1285-1292, May 1964.
30. N. K. Kul'man and R. L. Stratonovich, "Phase Automatic Frequency Control and Optimal Measurement of Narrow-Band Signal Parameters with Nonconstant Frequency in the Presence of Noise," *Radio Eng. and Elec. Physics*, **1**, 52-60, Jan. 1964.
31. H. J. Kushner, "On the Differential Equations Satisfied by Conditional Probability Densities of Markov Processes, with Applications," *J. SIAM Control*, Ser. A, **2**, No. 1, 106-119, 1964.

32. H. J. Kushner, "On the Dynamical Equations of Conditional Probability Density Functions, with Applications to Optimal Stochastic Control Theory," *J. Math. Anal. and Appl.*, 332-344, Apr. 1964.
33. H. J. Kushner, "The Exact Dynamical Equations Satisfied by the Conditional Mode," *IEEE Trans. Auto. Cont.*, **AC-12**, No. 3, 262-267, June 1967.
34. H. J. Kushner, "Approximations to Optimal Nonlinear Filters," *IEEE Trans. Auto. Cont.*, **AC-12**, No. 5, 546-556, Oct. 1967.
35. F. W. Lehan and R. J. Parks, "Optimum Demodulation," *IRE Nat. Conv. Rec.*, Pt. 8, 101-103, 1953.
36. J. D. McLean, S. F. Schmidt, and L. A. McGee, "Optimal Filtering and Linear Prediction Applied to a Midcourse Navigation System for the Circumlunar Mission," Ames Research Ctr., Moffett Field, Calif., NASA TN D-1208, Mar. 1962.
37. V. O. Mowrey, "Least Squares Recursive Differential-Correction Estimation in Nonlinear Problems," *IEEE Trans. Auto. Cont.*, **AC-10**, No. 4, pp. 399-407, Oct. 1965.
38. A. V. Skorokhod, *Studies in the Theory of Random Processes*, Addison-Wesley Publishing Co., Inc., Reading, Mass., 1965.
39. G. L. Smith, S. F. Schmidt, and L. A. McGee, "Applications of Statistical Filter Theory to the Optimal Estimation of Position and Velocity on Board a Circumlunar Vehicle," Ames Research Ctr., Moffett Field, Calif., NASA TR R-135, 1962.
40. D. L. Snyder, "Some Useful Expressions for Optimum Linear Filtering in White Noise," *Proc. IEEE*, **53**, 6, 629-630, June 1965.
41. D. L. Snyder, "An Application of an Equation for the Conditional Probability Density Functional of Markov Process to Nonlinear Minimum-Variance Filtering and Estimation," QPR No. 78, Research Laboratory of Electronics, M.I.T., Cambridge, Mass., July 1965.
42. D. L. Snyder, "Some Useful Expressions for Optimum Linear Filtering in White Noise: II," *Proc. IEEE*, **53**, 9, 1254-1255, Sept. 1965.
43. D. L. Snyder, "The State-Variable Approach to Continuous Estimation," Ph.D. Thesis, Department of Electrical Engineering, M.I.T., Cambridge, Mass., Feb. 1966.
44. D. L. Snyder, "Optimum Linear Filtering of an Integrated Signal in White Noise," *IEEE Trans. Aerospace and Electronic Systems*, **AES-2**, No. 2, 231-2, Mar. 1966.
45. D. L. Snyder, "A Theory of Continuous Nonlinear Recursive Filtering with Application to Optimum Analog Demodulation," *Proc. 1966 WESCON*, Pt. 1, Aug. 1966.
46. R. L. Stratonovich, "On the Theory of Optimal Nonlinear Filtration of Random Functions," *Th. of Prob. and Its Appl.*, **4**, 223-225, 1959.

47. R. L. Stratonovich, "Optimum Nonlinear Systems Which Bring about a Separation of a Signal with Constant Parameters from Noise," *Radiofizika*, **II**, No. 6, 892-901, 1959.
48. R. L. Stratonovich, "Application of the Theory of Markov Processes to Optimal Signal Discrimination," *Radio Eng. and Electronics*, **5**, No. 11, 1751-1763, 1960.
49. R. L. Stratonovich, "Conditional Markov Processes," *Th. Prob. and Its Appl.*, **5**, 2, 156-178, 1960.
50. R. L. Stratonovich, "A New Representation for Stochastic Integrals and Equations," *J. SIAM Control*, **4**, 2, 362-371, Aug. 1966.
51. J. B. Thomas and E. Wong, "On the Statistical Theory of Optimum Demodulation," *IRE Trans. Info. Th.*, **IT-6**, 420-425, Sept. 1960.
52. V. I. Tikhonov, "The Effect of Noise on Phase-Locked Oscillator Operation," *Automatika i Telemekhanika*, **20**, 9, 1959.
53. V. I. Tikhonov, "Phase Locked Automatic Frequency Control Operation in the Presence of Noise," *Automatika i Telemekhanika*, **21**, 1, 1960.
54. V. I. Tikhonov, "Nonlinear Filtration and Quasioptimal Nature of Frequency Phase Autotuning," *News of the Acad. of Sci., USSR*, 121-138, July 1965. (Also available as NASA STAR Report N65-27987.)
55. H. L. Van Trees, "An Introduction to Feedback Demodulation," TR 65G-5, Lincoln Laboratory, M.I.T., Cambridge, Mass., Aug. 1963.
56. H. L. Van Trees, "The Structure of Efficient Demodulators for Multidimensional Phase Modulated Signals," *IEEE Trans. Comm. Sys.*, 261-271, Sept. 1963.
57. H. L. Van Trees, "A Comparison of Optimum Angle Modulation Systems and Rate Distortion Bounds," *Proc. IEEE*, **53**, 12, Dec. 1965.
58. H. L. Van Trees, "Analog Communication over Randomly Time-Varying Channels," *IEEE Trans. Inf. Th.*, **IT-12**, No. 1, 51-63, Jan. 1966.
59. H. L. Van Trees, *Detection, Estimation and Modulation Theory: Part I*, John Wiley & Sons, Inc., New York, 1967.
60. H. L. Van Trees, *Detection, Estimation, and Modulation Theory: Part II*, John Wiley & Sons, Inc., New York, 1968.
61. A. J. Viterbi, "Phase-Lock Loop Dynamics in the Presence of Noise by Fokker-Planck Techniques," *Proc. IEEE*, **51**, 12, 1963.
62. A. Viterbi, "On the Minimum-Mean-Square Error Resulting from Linear Filtering of Stationary Signals in White Noise," *IEEE Trans. Info. Th.*, **IT-11**, No. 4, 594-595, Oct. 1965.
63. A. Viterbi and C. Cahn, "Optimum Coherent Phase and Frequency Demodulation of a Class of Modulating Spectra," *IEEE Trans. Space Electr. Telem.*, **10**, No. 3, 95-102, 1964.

64. C. S. Weaver, "Estimating and Detecting the Outputs of Linear Dynamical Systems," TR No. 6302-7, Systems Theory Lab., Stanford University, Stanford, Calif., 1964. (Also available as AD 464023 from DDC.)
65. N. Wiener, *The Extrapolation, Interpolation, and Smoothing of Stationary Time Series*, John Wiley & Sons, Inc., New York, 1949.
66. W. M. Wonham, "Some Applications of Stochastic Differential Equations to Optimal Nonlinear Filtering," *RIAS TR 64-3*, Baltimore, Md., Feb. 1964.
67. W. M. Wonham, "Some Applications of Stochastic Differential Equations to Optimal Nonlinear Filtering," *J. SIAM Control*. Ser. **A**, 2, 3, 347-369, 1965.
68. E. Wong and M. Zakai, "On Convergence of the Solutions of Differential Equations Involving Brownian Motion," Report No. 65-5, E.R.L., University of California, Berkeley, Calif., Jan. 1965.
69. D. C. Youla, "The Use of Maximum Likelihood in Estimating Continuously Modulated Intelligence Which Has Been Corrupted by Noise," *IRE Trans. Info. Th.*, **IT-3**, 90-105, Mar. 1954.
70. M. Yovits and J. Jackson, "Linear Filter Optimization with Game Theory Considerations," *1955 IRE Nat. Conv. Rec.*, **3**, 4, 193-199.
71. L. Zadeh and C. Desoer, *Linear System Theory*, McGraw-Hill Book Co., New York, 1963.
72. R. Zaorski, "Simulation of Analog Demodulation Systems," S. M. Thesis, Department of Electrical Engineering, M.I.T., Cambridge, Mass., Feb. 1965.

Index